D0188566

It's another cracking book from CGP...

Edexcel's 9-1 International GCSE in Chemistry is pretty tough going, but this brilliant CGP book has it sorted. We explain every topic in our clear, straightforward style, and we've included plenty of practice questions to sharpen up your exam skills.

It's great for the Edexcel International GCSE Science Double Award too!

How to access your free Online Edition

This book includes a free Online Edition to read on your PC, Mac or tablet.
To access it, just go to **cgpbooks.co.uk/extras** and enter this code...

2548 7099 1646 4035

By the way, this code only works for one person. If somebody else has used this book before you, they might have already claimed the Online Edition.

CGP — still the best! ☺

Our sole aim here at CGP is to produce the highest quality books —
carefully written, immaculately presented and dangerously close to being funny.

Then we work our socks off to get them out to you
— at the cheapest possible prices.

Contents

Section 6 — Organic Chemistry

Describing Experiments

Paper 2

This book covers both Chemistry Paper 1 and Chemistry
Paper 2 material. Some material is needed for Paper 2 only —
we've clearly marked this in green boxes like this one.
The Paper 2 revision questions in the book are also printed in green.
If you're doing a Science (Double Award) qualification
you don't need to learn the Paper 2 material.

Paper 2

Published by CGP.
From original material by Paddy Gannon.

Editors: Alex Billings, Robin Flello and Sarah Pattison

Contributors: Mike Thompson

ISBN: 978 1 78294 676 2

With thanks to Katherine Faudemer, Rachel Kordan and Jamie Sinclair for the proofreading.

With thanks to Ana Pungartnik for the copyright research.

Graph to show trend in Atmospheric CO_2 Concentration and global temperature on page 40
based on data by EPICA community members 2004 and Siegenthaler et al 2005.

Printed by Elanders Ltd, Newcastle upon Tyne.
Clipart from Corel®

Based on the classic CGP style created by Richard Parsons.

States of Matter

You can explain quite a bit of the stuff in chemistry if you can get your head round this lot.

The Three States of Matter — Solid, Liquid and Gas

Materials come in <u>three</u> different forms — <u>solid</u>, <u>liquid</u> and <u>gas</u>. These are the <u>Three States of Matter</u>. Which <u>state</u> you get (<u>solid</u>, <u>liquid</u> or <u>gas</u>) depends on how <u>strong</u> the forces of attraction are between the particles of the material. How strong the forces are depends on <u>THREE THINGS</u>:
  a) the <u>material</u>   b) the <u>temperature</u>   c) the <u>pressure</u>.

Solids

1) In solids, there are <u>strong forces</u> of attraction between particles, which holds them <u>close together</u> in <u>fixed positions</u> to form a very regular <u>lattice arrangement</u>.

2) The particles <u>don't move</u> from their positions, so all solids keep a <u>definite shape</u> and <u>volume</u>, and don't flow like liquids.

3) The particles <u>vibrate</u> about their positions — the <u>hotter</u> the solid becomes, the <u>more</u> they vibrate (causing solids to <u>expand</u> slightly when heated).

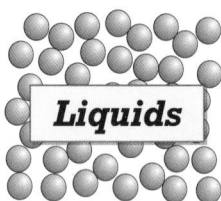

Liquids

1) In liquids, there is a <u>weak force</u> of attraction between the particles. They're randoml|
arranged and <u>free</u> to <u>move</u> past each other, but they tend to <u>stick closely together</u>|

2) Liquids have a definite volume but <u>don't</u> keep a <u>definite shape</u>, and will flow to fill the bottom of a container.

3) The particles are <u>constantly</u> moving with <u>random motion</u>. The <u>hotter</u> the liquid gets, the <u>faster</u> they move. This causes liquids to <u>expand</u> slightly when heated.

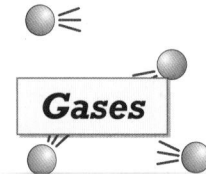

Gases

1) In gases, the force of attraction between the particles is <u>very weak</u> — they're <u>free</u> to <u>move</u> and are <u>far apart</u>. The particles in gases travel in <u>straight lines</u>.

2) Gases <u>don't</u> keep a definite <u>shape</u> or <u>volume</u> and will always <u>fill</u> any container.

3) The particles move <u>constantly</u> with <u>random motion</u>. The <u>hotter</u> the gas gets, the <u>faster</u> they move. Gases either <u>expand</u> when heated, or their <u>pressure increases</u>.

Substances Can Change from One State to Another

The red arrows show heat being added. The blue arrows show heat being given out.

<u>Physical changes</u> don't change the particles — just their <u>arrangement</u> or their <u>energy</u>.

3) At a certain temperature, the particles have <u>enough energy</u> to <u>break</u> free from their positions. This is called <u>melting</u> and the solid turns into a <u>liquid</u>.

2) This makes the particles <u>vibrate more</u>, which <u>weakens</u> the <u>forces</u> that hold the solid together. This makes the solid <u>expand</u>.

1) When a <u>solid</u> is <u>heated</u>, its particles <u>gain</u> more <u>energy</u>.

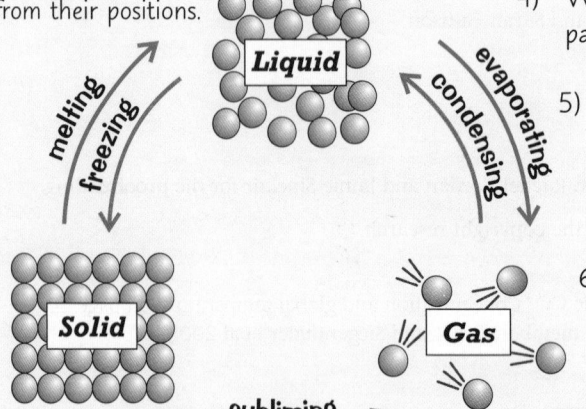

4) When a liquid is <u>heated</u>, again the particles get even <u>more energy</u>.

5) This energy makes the particles <u>move faster</u>, which <u>weakens</u> and <u>breaks</u> the <u>bonds</u> holding the liquid together.

6) At a certain temperature, the particles have enough energy to <u>break</u> their <u>bonds</u>. This is called <u>evaporating</u> and the liquid turns into a <u>gas</u>.

Phew, what a page — particle-ularly gripping stuff...

Time to get to the bottom of the matter with all these states of matter. Try your hand at this question...

Q1   What states of matter are you moving from and to if you are condensing a substance?   [1 mark]

Movement of Particles

There are many nifty experiments that you can do to observe the wonders of chemistry. Here are a few...

Diffusion is the Movement of Particles Through a Liquid or Gas

Diffusion is the gradual movement of particles from places where there are lots of them to places where there are fewer of them. It's just the natural tendency for stuff to spread out. You can use the experiments below to demonstrate diffusion...

Potassium Manganate(VII) and Water

Potassium manganate(VII) is great for this experiment because it's bright purple.

  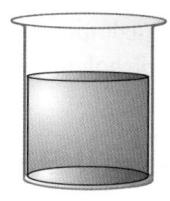

1) If you take a beaker of water and place some potassium manganate(VII) at the bottom, the purple colour slowly spreads out to fill the beaker.

2) This is chemistry in action (groan)... The particles of potassium manganate(VII) are diffusing out among the particles of water.

3) It's the random motion of particles in a liquid (see the previous page) that causes the purple colour to eventually be evenly spread out throughout the water.

> If you were to add more water to the final purple solution, the potassium manganate(VII) particles would spread even further apart and the solution would be less purple. This is called dilution.

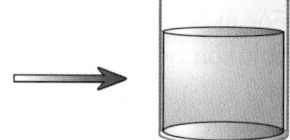

Ammonia and Hydrogen Chloride

1) Aqueous ammonia (NH₃) gives off ammonia gas. Hydrochloric acid (HCl) gives off hydrogen chloride gas.

2) If you set up an experiment like this...

...you'll get a white ring of ammonium chloride forming in the glass tube.

glass tube

cotton wool soaked in hydrochloric acid

cotton wool soaked in aqueous ammonia

ring of ammonium chloride

3) The NH_3 gas diffuses from one end of the tube and the HCl gas diffuses from the other. When they meet they react to form ammonium chloride.

4) The ring doesn't form exactly in the middle of the glass tube — it forms nearest the end of the tube where the hydrochloric acid was.

5) This is because the particles of ammonia are smaller and lighter than the particles of hydrogen chloride, so they diffuse through the air more quickly.

Since ammonia diffuses more quickly, it will travel further than HCl in the same amount of time.

Bromine Gas and Air

1) Bromine gas is a brown, strongly smelling gas. You can use it to demonstrate diffusion in gases.

2) Fill half a gas jar full of bromine gas, and the other half full of air — separate the gases with a glass plate.

3) When you remove the glass plate, you'll see the brown bromine gas slowly diffusing through the air.

4) The random motion of the particles means that the bromine will eventually diffuse right through the air.

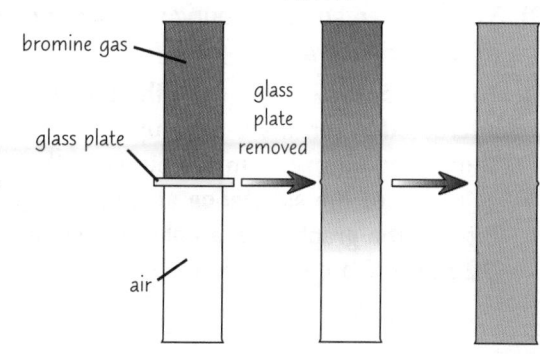

bromine gas

glass plate

glass plate removed

air

Sleeping on the book doesn't make the words diffuse into your head...

Make sure you know how the particles move about in these experiments — it'll help you to explain the results.

Q1   Describe and explain what happens when a spatula of potassium manganate(VII) is added to water.   [2 marks]

Solutions

This page is all about <u>solutions</u>. Study it carefully and you might even get some solutions to exam questions...

A Solution is a Mixture of Solvent and Solute

When you add a <u>solid</u> (the <u>solute</u>) to a <u>liquid</u> (the <u>solvent</u>) the bonds holding the solute molecules together <u>sometimes break</u> and the molecules then <u>mix</u> with the molecules in the liquid — forming a <u>solution</u>. This is called <u>dissolving</u>. Make sure you learn these important <u>definitions</u>:

1) <u>Solution</u> – is a mixture of a solute and a solvent that does not separate out.
2) <u>Solute</u> – is the substance being dissolved.
3) <u>Solvent</u> – is the liquid it's dissolving into.
4) <u>Saturated solution</u> – a solution where the maximum amount of solute has been dissolved, so no more solute will dissolve in the solution.

Solubility is a Measure of How Much Solute will Dissolve in a Solvent

1) The ability of a <u>substance</u> to <u>dissolve</u> in a solvent is known as its <u>solubility</u>.
2) Solubility is often measured in <u>grams of solute</u> per <u>100 grams of solvent</u>.
3) For example, if 23 grams of a substance can dissolve in 100 grams of water before the solution becomes <u>saturated</u>, that substance has a solubility of 23 g per 100 g of water.
4) The <u>solubility</u> of most solid substances <u>increases</u> as you increase the <u>temperature</u>.
5) A graph of solubility versus temperature is known as a <u>solubility curve</u>:

Solubility goes up the y-axis.

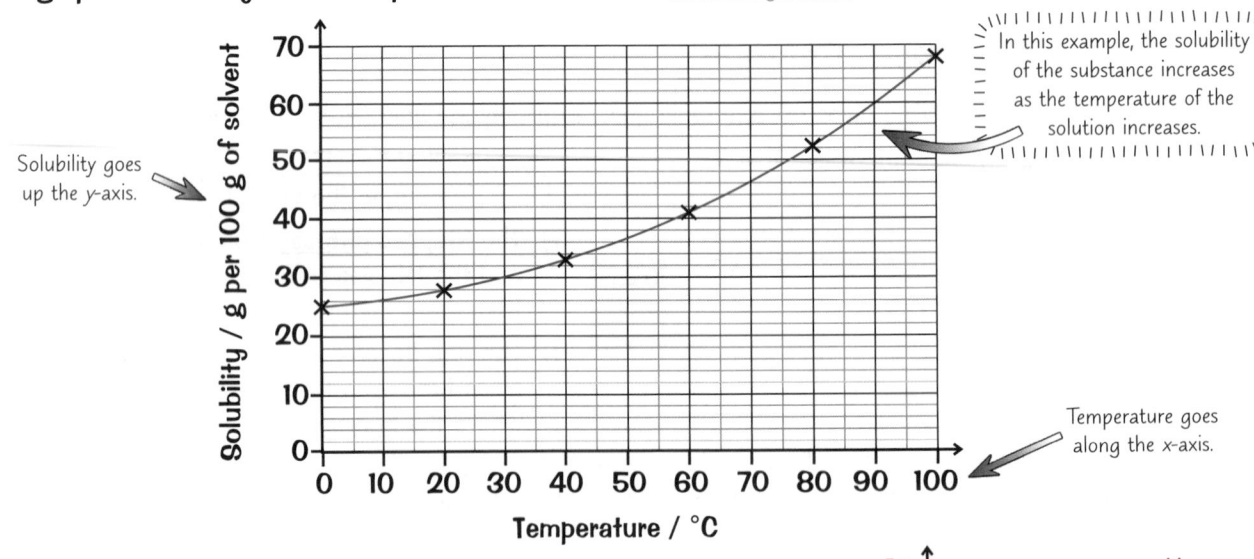

In this example, the solubility of the substance increases as the temperature of the solution increases.

Temperature goes along the x-axis.

6) You can use solubility curves to see the solubility of a substance at a <u>specific temperature</u>.
7) To do this, draw a <u>line</u> from the temperature that you're interested in (on the x-axis) up to the <u>curve</u>. Then, <u>read across</u> from the curve to the y-axis to find the <u>solubility</u> of the substance at that <u>particular temperature</u>. E.g. on the graph on the right, the solubility at 25 °C is 32 g per 100 g of solvent.

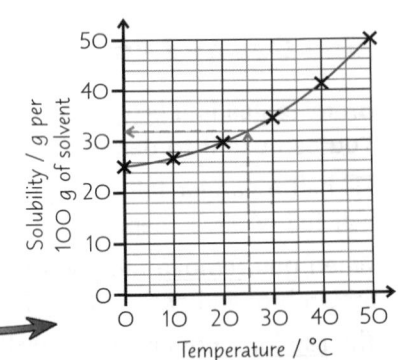

How do dissolved soldiers greet their General? They give a solute...

Learning all the definitions in chemistry can be a right pain, but it's worth it for those juicy marks in the exam.

Q1   Describe the difference between a solvent and a solute.   [2 marks]

Q2   What is meant by the 'solubility' of a substance?   [1 mark]

Paper 2

P2

Investigating Solubility

You can measure <u>solubility</u> by <u>evaporating</u> away all the water in a solution. Sounds weird, but trust me...

You can Investigate how Temperature Affects Solubility

Here's how you would investigate how the <u>solubility</u> of <u>ammonium chloride</u> (a solid) is affected by <u>temperature</u>:

1) Make a <u>saturated solution</u> by adding an <u>excess</u> of ammonium chloride to 10 cm³ of <u>water</u> in a boiling tube.
   You will know when ammonium chloride is in excess because it will start to <u>sink</u> to the bottom of the tube.

2) Give the solution a good <u>stir</u> and place the boiling tube in a <u>water bath</u> set to 25 °C.

3) After <u>5 minutes</u>, check that <u>all</u> of the excess solid
   has sunk to the <u>bottom</u> of the tube and use a
   <u>thermometer</u> to check that the solution has reached 25 °C.

4) <u>Weigh</u> an <u>empty evaporating basin</u>. Pour some of the solution
   into the basin, making sure not to pour in any of the <u>undissolved solid</u>.

ammonium chloride solution

evaporating basin

Bunsen burner

5) <u>Re-weigh</u> the basin and its contents, then gently <u>heat</u> it
   using a <u>Bunsen burner</u> to remove all the water.
   If you heat the basin too strongly, some of the ammonium chloride might turn into a gas and escape.
   This will cause the mass of solid in the basin to decrease, and your solubility value will be lower than it should be.

6) Once all the water has <u>evaporated</u>, you're left with <u>pure ammonium chloride</u>.
   <u>Re-weigh</u> the evaporating basin and its contents.

7) <u>Repeat</u> steps 1-6 twice more, but with the water bath at <u>different</u> temperatures (e.g. 35 °C and 45 °C).

8) You can use the different masses to work out the <u>solubility</u> at each <u>temperature</u> — see below.

9) You could plot the results on a <u>graph</u> like the one on the previous page.

Paper 2

You can Calculate the Solubility from the Masses of the Solid and Water

You can use the following equation to calculate the <u>solubility</u> from the <u>results</u> of the experiment above:

$$\text{solubility (g per 100 g of solvent)} = \frac{\text{mass of solid (g)}}{\text{mass of water removed (g)}} \times 100$$

Example: A student dries a saturated solution of ammonium chloride that was prepared at 25 °C.
Use the following experimental data to find the solubility of ammonium chloride at 25 °C.

Mass of evaporating basin	78.6 g
Mass of evaporating basin + saturated solution	89.3 g
Mass of evaporating basin + solid	81.5 g

Method:

1) Find the <u>mass of solid left over</u> in the basin:
   mass of solid = (mass of evaporating basin + solid) − mass of evaporating basin
   = 81.5 g − 78.6 g = 2.9 g

2) Find the <u>mass of water removed</u> during evaporation:
   mass of water removed = (mass of basin + saturated solution) − (mass of basin + solid)
   = 89.3 g − 81.5 g = 7.8 g

3) Use the equation above to calculate the <u>solubility</u>:
   solubility = (mass of solid ÷ mass of water removed) × 100
   = (2.9 ÷ 7.8) × 100 = 37.1794... = <u>37 g per 100 g of water</u>

Adding some sugar to your morning beverage — solubilitea...

Who knows, you might be lucky enough to get to do this experiment in class. Wouldn't that be exciting...

Q1   Describe an experiment that could be used to determine the solubility of a solid at 40 °C.   [5 marks] [P2]

Atoms

All substances are made of <u>atoms</u>. They're really <u>tiny</u> — too small to see, even with a microscope.

Atoms Contain Protons, Neutrons and Electrons

The atom is made up of three <u>subatomic particles</u> — protons, neutrons and electrons.

- <u>Protons</u> are <u>heavy</u> and <u>positively charged</u>.
- <u>Neutrons</u> are <u>heavy</u> and <u>neutral</u>.
- <u>Electrons</u> have <u>hardly any mass</u> and are <u>negatively charged</u>.

Particle	Relative mass	Relative charge
Proton	1	+1
Neutron	1	0
Electron	0.0005	−1

Relative mass (measured in atomic mass units) measures mass on a scale where the mass of a proton or neutron is 1.

Protons and neutrons are still teeny tiny — they're just heavy compared to electrons.

The Nucleus

1) It's in the <u>middle</u> of the atom.
2) It contains <u>protons</u> and <u>neutrons</u>.
3) It has a <u>positive charge</u> because of the protons.
4) Almost the <u>whole</u> mass of the atom is <u>concentrated</u> in the nucleus.
5) Compared to the overall size of the atom, the nucleus is <u>tiny</u>.

The Electrons

1) Electrons move <u>around</u> the nucleus in energy levels called <u>shells</u>.
2) They're <u>negatively charged</u>.
3) They're <u>tiny</u>, but their orbitals cover <u>a lot of space</u>.
4) The <u>size</u> of their orbitals determines the size of the atom.
5) Electrons have virtually <u>no</u> mass (so small that it's sometimes given as zero).

Houston, we're in orbit.

Number of Electrons Equals Number of Protons

1) Neutral atoms have <u>no charge</u> overall.
2) The <u>charge</u> on the electrons is the <u>same</u> size as the charge on the <u>protons</u> — but <u>opposite</u>.
3) This means the <u>number</u> of <u>electrons</u> always equals the <u>number</u> of <u>protons</u> in a <u>neutral atom</u>.
4) If some electrons are <u>added or removed</u>, the atom becomes <u>charged</u> and is then an <u>ion</u>.

Atomic Number and Mass Number Describe an Atom

These two numbers tell you how many of each kind of particle an atom has.

1) The <u>atomic number</u> tells you how many <u>protons</u> there are.
2) Atoms of the <u>same</u> element all have the <u>same</u> number of <u>protons</u> — so atoms of <u>different</u> elements will have <u>different</u> numbers of <u>protons</u>.
3) The <u>mass number</u> is the total of <u>protons</u> and <u>neutrons</u> in the atom.
4) To get the number of <u>neutrons</u>, just <u>subtract</u> the <u>atomic number</u> from the <u>mass number</u>.

Mass number → 23
Atomic number → 11
Na — Element symbol

Molecules are Groups of Atoms

1) Atoms can join together to form <u>molecules</u>.
2) Some molecules are made from just <u>one element</u> (e.g. H_2, N_2), while others are made up of <u>more than one element</u> (e.g. H_2O, CO_2).

Molecules are held together by covalent bonds (see pages 18-20 for more).

Don't trust atoms — they make up everything...

You need to learn what's in that table with the relative masses and relative charges of the different parts of the atom.

Q1 A certain neutral atom of potassium has an atomic number of 19 and a mass number of 39. Give the number of electrons, protons and neutrons in the atom. [3 marks]

Isotopes and Relative Atomic Mass

Atoms were reasonably straightforward weren't they? Think again. Here come isotopes to confuse everything.

Isotopes are the Same Except for an Extra Neutron or Two

A favourite exam question is: "Explain the meaning of the term isotope"
The trick is that it's impossible to explain what one isotope is. Nice of them that, isn't it!
You have to outsmart them and always start your answer "Isotopes are..." LEARN the definition:

> Isotopes are different atomic forms of the same element, which have the same number of protons but different numbers of neutrons.

1) The upshot is: isotopes must have the same proton number but different mass numbers.
2) If they had different proton numbers, they'd be different elements altogether.
3) A very popular example of a pair of isotopes is carbon-12 and carbon-13.

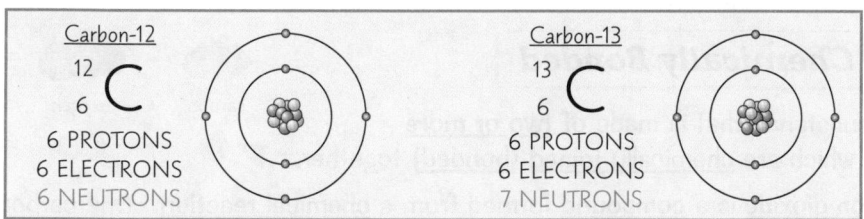

Remember — the number of neutrons is just the mass number minus the atomic number.

Relative Atomic Mass Takes All Stable Isotopes into Account

1) Relative atomic mass (A_r) is just a way of saying how heavy different atoms are compared with the mass of an atom of carbon-12. So carbon-12 has an A_r of exactly 12.
2) It's the average mass of all the isotopes of an element. It has to allow for the relative mass of each isotope and its relative abundance.
3) Relative abundance just means how much there is of each isotope compared to the total amount of the element in the world. This can be a ratio, a fraction or a percentage.

For example, you could calculate the relative atomic mass of chlorine using the info in the table below:

element	relative mass of isotope	relative abundance
chlorine	35.0	3
	37.0	1

This means that there are 2 isotopes of chlorine. One has a relative mass of 35 (^{35}Cl) and the other 37 (^{37}Cl).

The relative abundances show that there are 3 atoms of ^{35}Cl to every 1 of ^{37}Cl.

1) Multiply the mass of each isotope by its relative abundance.
2) Add those together.
3) Divide by the sum of the relative abundances.

$$A_r = \frac{(35.0 \times 3) + (37.0 \times 1)}{3 + 1} = 35.5$$

4) You can find the relative atomic mass of any element using the periodic table (see p.13).
5) Relative atomic masses don't usually come out as whole numbers or easy decimals, but they're often rounded to the nearest 0.5 in periodic tables.

Will this be in your exam? — isotope so...

Remember, isotopes have the same proton number but different mass numbers — you're gonna need to learn it.

Q1 Bromine has an atomic number of 35 and has two stable isotopes — bromine-79 and bromine-81.
Given that 51% of bromine atoms are bromine-79, and 49% are bromine-81,
work out the relative atomic mass of bromine. Give your answer to the nearest whole number. [2 marks]

Elements, Compounds and Mixtures

There are only about <u>100 or so</u> different kinds of atoms, which doesn't sound too bad.
But they can <u>join together</u> in <u>loads</u> of different combinations, which makes life more complicated.

Elements Consist of One Type of Atom Only

Quite a lot of everyday substances are <u>elements</u>:

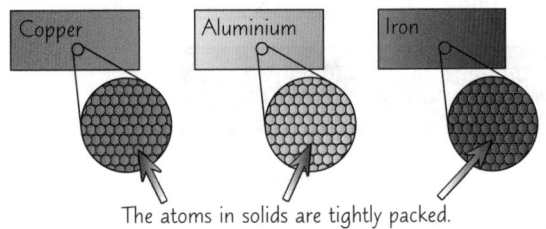

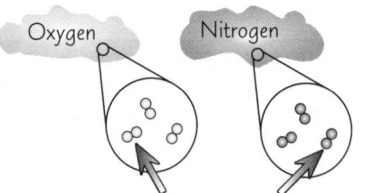

Nitrogen is the most common element in the air (about 78%).

The atoms in solids are tightly packed.

Atoms in gases often go round in pairs. A molecule with two atoms in it is called a diatomic molecule.

Compounds are Chemically Bonded

1) A <u>compound</u> is a substance that is made of <u>two or more</u> <u>different elements</u> which are <u>chemically joined</u> (<u>bonded</u>) together.

carbon + oxygen ⟶ carbon dioxide

2) For example, <u>carbon dioxide</u> is a <u>compound</u> formed from a <u>chemical reaction</u>. One carbon atom reacts with two oxygen atoms to form a <u>molecule</u> of carbon dioxide, with the <u>formula</u> CO_2.

3) It's <u>very difficult</u> to <u>separate</u> the two original elements out again.

4) The <u>properties</u> of a compound are often <u>totally different</u> from the properties of the <u>original elements</u>.

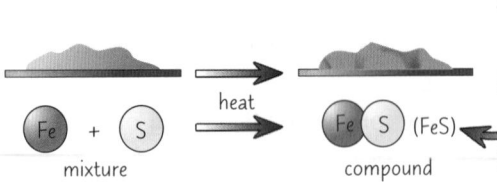

mixture   compound

5) For example, if a mixture of iron and sulfur is <u>heated</u>, the iron and sulfur atoms react to form the compound <u>iron sulfide</u> (**FeS**).

6) Iron sulfide is not much like iron (e.g. it's not attracted to a magnet), nor is it much like sulfur (e.g. it's not yellow in colour).

Mixtures are Easily Separated — Not Like Compounds

1) Unlike in a compound, there's <u>no chemical bond</u> between the different parts of a mixture. The parts can be separated out by <u>physical methods</u> such as distillation (see page 11).

2) The <u>properties</u> of a mixture are just a <u>mixture</u> of the properties of the <u>separate parts</u>. E.g. a <u>mixture</u> of <u>iron powder</u> and <u>sulfur powder</u> will show the properties of <u>both iron and sulfur</u>. It will contain grey magnetic bits of iron and bright yellow bits of sulfur.

Iron and sulfur mixed together, but unreacted.

A Mixture Isn't a Pure Substance

1) In chemistry, a substance is <u>pure</u> if it's completely made up of a <u>single element or compound</u>.

2) Every <u>pure</u> substance has a <u>specific, sharp melting point</u> and <u>boiling point</u>. For example, pure ice melts at 0 °C, and pure water boils at 100 °C.

3) A <u>mixture</u> is <u>not</u> pure — it will melt or boil <u>gradually</u> over a <u>range</u> of temperatures.

Not learning this stuff will only compound your problems...

Sometimes it's easiest to explain things in chemistry using examples. If you understand the difference between the mixture of iron powder and sulfur powder, and the compound iron sulfide, it'll make all this stuff easier to remember.

Q1   State whether each of the following is an element, compound or mixture:
a) carbon dioxide gas   b) chlorine gas   c) air   [3 marks]

Filtration and Crystallisation

The components of mixtures are <u>not</u> chemically joined (see p.8), so can be <u>separated</u> using <u>physical methods</u>.

Filtration is Used to Separate an Insoluble Solid from a Liquid

1) If the <u>product</u> of a reaction is an <u>insoluble solid</u>, you can use <u>filtration</u> to separate it out from the <u>liquid reaction mixture</u>.

2) It can be used in <u>purification</u> as well. For example, <u>solid impurities</u> can be separated out from a reaction mixture using <u>filtration</u>.

3) All you do is pop some <u>filter paper</u> into a <u>funnel</u> and pour your mixture into it. The liquid part of the mixture <u>runs through</u> the paper, leaving behind a <u>solid residue</u>.

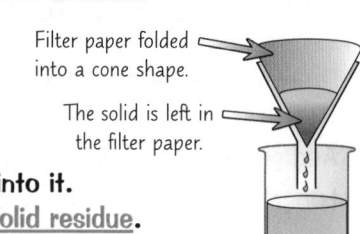

Filter paper folded into a cone shape.

The solid is left in the filter paper.

Crystallisation Separates a Soluble Solid from a Solution

Here's how you <u>crystallise</u> a product...

1) Pour the solution into an <u>evaporating dish</u> and gently <u>heat</u> the solution. Some of the <u>water</u> will evaporate and the solution will get more <u>concentrated</u>.

2) Once some of the water has evaporated, <u>or</u> when you see crystals start to form (the <u>point of crystallisation</u>), remove the dish from the heat and leave the solution to <u>cool</u>.

3) The salt should start to form <u>crystals</u> as it becomes <u>insoluble</u> in the cold, highly concentrated solution.

4) <u>Filter</u> the crystals out of the solution, and leave them in a warm place to <u>dry</u>. You could also use a <u>drying oven</u> or a <u>desiccator</u> (a desiccator contains chemicals that remove water from the surroundings).

evaporating dish

You Can Use Filtration and Crystallisation to Separate Rock Salt

1) <u>Rock salt</u> is simply a <u>mixture</u> of <u>salt</u> and <u>sand</u> (they spread it on the roads in winter).

2) Salt and sand are both <u>compounds</u> — but <u>salt dissolves</u> in water and <u>sand doesn't</u>. This <u>vital difference</u> in their <u>physical properties</u> gives a great way to <u>separate</u> them.

3) Here's how you would do it:

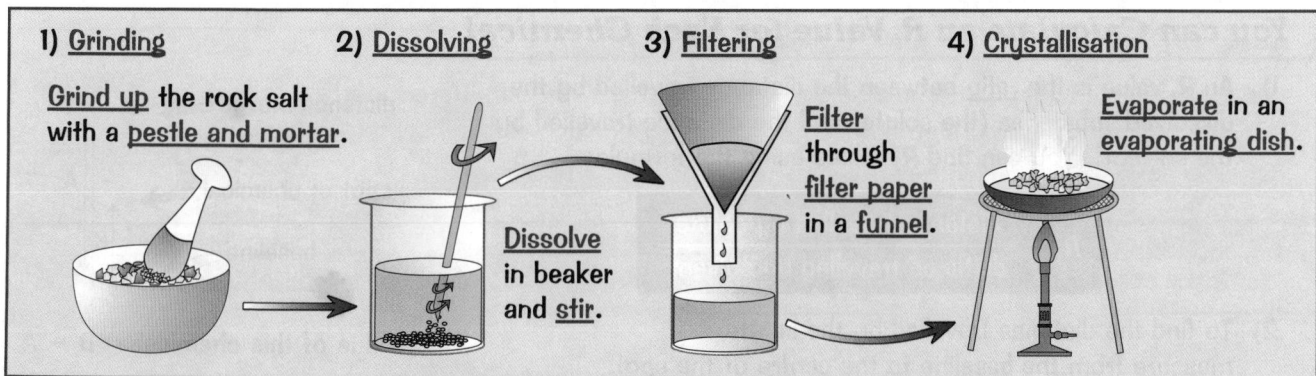

1) <u>Grinding</u>

<u>Grind up</u> the rock salt with a <u>pestle and mortar</u>.

2) <u>Dissolving</u>

<u>Dissolve</u> in beaker and <u>stir</u>.

3) <u>Filtering</u>

<u>Filter</u> through <u>filter paper</u> in a <u>funnel</u>.

4) <u>Crystallisation</u>

<u>Evaporate</u> in an <u>evaporating dish</u>.

4) The sand doesn't dissolve (it's <u>insoluble</u>), so it stays as <u>big grains</u>. These <u>won't fit</u> through the <u>tiny holes</u> in the filter paper — so it <u>collects on the filter paper</u>.

5) The <u>salt</u> is dissolved in <u>solution</u>, so it does go through — and when the water's <u>evaporated</u>, the salt forms as <u>crystals</u> in the <u>evaporating dish</u>.

Revise mixtures — just filter out the important bits...

One page on separation down, and a couple more to come. But hold your horses... Before you dash on to the next page (I know, I know, it's just so exciting), make sure you've learnt all the details on this page first.

Q1   You are given a solution that has been made by dissolving copper sulfate crystals in water. Describe a method that you could use to extract pure copper sulfate crystals from the solution.   [4 marks]

Chromatography

Chromatography is another method used by chemists to separate out mixtures. You can use paper chromatography to separate out dyes — e.g. in inks, paints, food colourings etc. It's, er, fascinating stuff.

You Need to Know How to Do Paper Chromatography

PRACTICAL

1) Draw a line near the bottom of a sheet of filter paper — this is the baseline.
   (Use a pencil to do this — pencil marks are insoluble so won't dissolve in the solvent.)

2) Add spots of different inks to the line at regular intervals.

3) Loosely roll the sheet up and put it in a beaker of solvent, e.g. water.

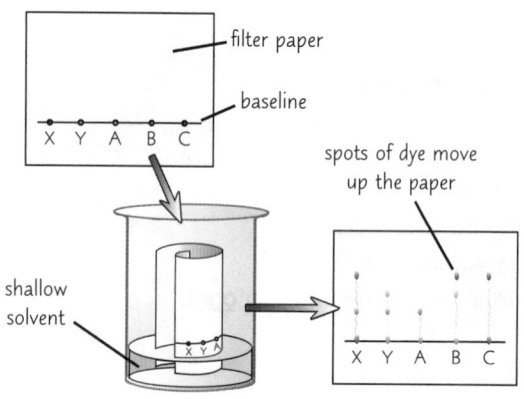

filter paper

baseline

X Y A B C

spots of dye move up the paper

shallow solvent

X Y A

X Y A B C

4) The solvent used depends on what's being tested. Some compounds dissolve well in water, but sometimes other solvents, like ethanol, are needed.

5) Make sure the level of solvent is below the baseline — you don't want the inks to dissolve into the solvent.

6) Place a lid on top of the container to stop the solvent evaporating.

7) The solvent seeps up the paper, carrying the inks with it.

8) Each different dye in the inks will move up the paper at a different rate and form a spot in a different place.

9) When the solvent has nearly reached the top of the paper, take the paper out of the beaker and leave it to dry.

10) The end result is a pattern of spots called a chromatogram.

How Chromatography Separates Mixtures...

1) Chromatography works because different dyes will move up the paper at different rates.

2) Some will stick to the paper and others will dissolve more readily in the solvent and travel more quickly.

3) The distance the dyes travel up the paper depends on the solvent and the paper you use.

You can Calculate an R_f Value for Each Chemical

1) An R_f value is the ratio between the distance travelled by the dissolved substance (the solute) and the distance travelled by the solvent. You can find R_f values using the formula:

$$R_f = \frac{\text{distance travelled by solute}}{\text{distance travelled by solvent}}$$

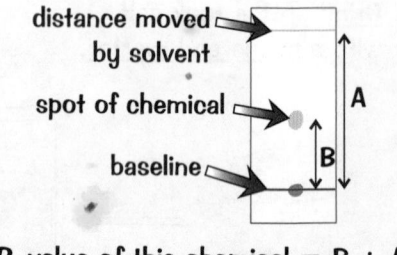

distance moved by solvent

spot of chemical

baseline

A

B

R_f value of this chemical = B ÷ A

2) To find the distance travelled by the solute, measure from the baseline to the centre of the spot.

3) Chromatography is often carried out to see if a certain substance is present in a mixture. You run a pure sample of a substance that you think might be in your mixture alongside a sample of the mixture itself. If the sample has the same R_f values as one of the spots, they're likely to be the same.

4) Chemists sometimes run samples of pure substances called standard reference materials (SRMs) next to a mixture to check the identities of its components. SRMs have controlled concentrations and purities.

Comb-atography — identifying mysterious things in your hair...

So that's chromatography — it's pretty neat once you get your head around it. You can use it for all kinds of things, like crime-fighting... CSIs use chromatography to identify unknown substances from crime scenes. Ain't science grand.

Q1   On a paper chromatogram, chemical X travelled 2.1 cm, chemical Y travelled 3.6 cm
      and the solvent travelled 6.0 cm. Calculate the R_f value of chemical Y. $\frac{3.6}{6} = 0.6$
                                                                                          [2 marks]

Distillation

Distillation is used to separate mixtures that contain <u>liquids</u>.
There are two types that you need to know about — <u>simple</u> and <u>fractional</u>.

Simple Distillation is Used to Separate Out Solutions

1) <u>Simple distillation</u> is used for separating out a <u>liquid</u> from a <u>solution</u>.

2) The solution is <u>heated</u>. The part of the solution that has the lowest boiling point <u>evaporates</u>.

3) The <u>vapour</u> is then <u>cooled</u>, <u>condenses</u> (turns back into a liquid) and is <u>collected</u>.

4) The rest of the <u>solution</u> is left behind in the flask.

5) You can use simple distillation to get <u>pure water</u> from <u>seawater</u>. The <u>water</u> evaporates and is condensed and collected. Eventually you'll end up with just the <u>salt</u> left in the flask.

6) The <u>problem</u> with simple distillation is that you can only use it to separate things with <u>very different</u> boiling points.

7) If you have a <u>mixture of liquids</u> with <u>similar boiling points</u>, you need another method to separate them out — like fractional distillation...

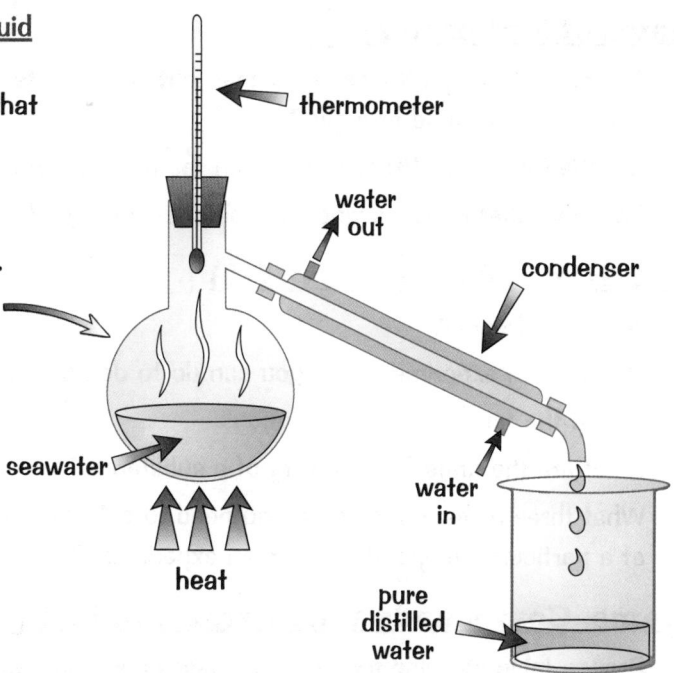

thermometer

water out

condenser

seawater

water in

heat

pure distilled water

Fractional Distillation is Used to Separate a Mixture of Liquids

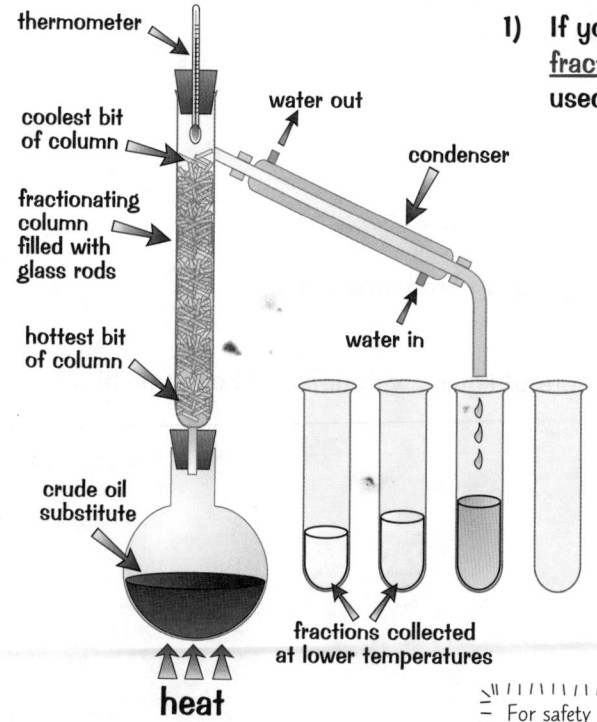

thermometer

coolest bit of column

water out

condenser

fractionating column filled with glass rods

hottest bit of column

water in

crude oil substitute

fractions collected at lower temperatures

heat

1) If you've got a <u>mixture of liquids</u> you can separate it using <u>fractional distillation</u>. Here is a lab demonstration that can be used to model <u>fractional distillation of crude oil</u> at a <u>refinery</u>.

2) You put your <u>mixture</u> in a flask and stick a <u>fractionating column</u> on top. Then you heat it.

3) The <u>different liquids</u> will all have <u>different boiling points</u> — so they will evaporate at <u>different temperatures</u>.

4) The liquid with the <u>lowest boiling point</u> evaporates first. When the temperature on the thermometer matches the boiling point of this liquid, it will reach the <u>top</u> of the column.

5) Liquids with <u>higher boiling points</u> might also start to evaporate. But the column is <u>cooler</u> towards the <u>top</u>. So they will only get part of the way up before <u>condensing</u> and running back down towards the flask.

6) When the first liquid has been collected, you <u>raise the temperature</u> until the <u>next one</u> reaches the top.

For safety reasons this experiment uses a substitute for real crude oil.

Fractionating — sounds a bit too much like maths to me...

Remember that parts of mixtures aren't joined together — so you can separate them by physical methods without the need for chemical reactions. And don't forget — you need to learn these separation techniques for the exam.

Q1   Propan-1-ol, methanol and ethanol have boiling points of 97 °C, <u>65 °C</u> and 78 °C respectively.
A student uses fractional distillation to separate a mixture of these compounds.
State which liquid will be collected in the first fraction and explain why.   [2 marks]

Revision Questions for Section 1

Congrats, that's the end of Section 1. And I always say, the first section is always, well sometimes, the hardest...

- Try these questions and tick off each one when you get it right.
- When you've done all the questions under a heading and are completely happy with it, tick it off.

States of Matter (p.2) ☑

1) A substance keeps the same volume, but changes its shape according to the container it's in. Is it a solid, a liquid or a gas? ☑

2) Are the forces of attraction between the particles in a liquid stronger or weaker than those in a gas? ☑

3) Describe what happens when a substance changes from a liquid to a gas. ☑

Diffusion and Solutions (p.3-5) ☐

4) What is diffusion? ☑

5) Describe an experiment that you can do to demonstrate diffusion. ☑

6) Define the term 'saturated solution'.

7) What are the units for solubility of a substance?

8) What three measurements do you need to calculate the solubility of a substance at a particular temperature from an experiment? ☑

Atoms, Compounds and Mixtures (p.6-8) ☐

9) Draw a table showing the relative masses and charges of the three types of particle in an atom. ☑

10) Sketch the nuclear model of an atom. Give three details about the nucleus and three details about the electrons. ☑

11) What do the mass number and atomic number of an element tell you? ☑

12) What is an isotope? ☑

13) Describe the difference between a mixture and a compound. ☑

Separation Techniques (p.9-11) ☑

14) Describe how to carry out filtration. ☐

15) Describe how you could separate the dyes in some inks using paper chromatography. ☑

16) Give the formula for calculating R_f values. ☑

17) Name the physical method you could use to separate a mixture of liquids with different boiling points. ☑

The Periodic Table

In 1869, <u>Dmitri Mendeleev</u> arranged 50 known elements in order of <u>atomic mass</u> to make a Table of Elements. Mendeleev's table placed elements with <u>similar chemical properties</u> in the same vertical <u>groups</u> — but he found that he had to leave <u>gaps</u> in his table to make this work. The gaps in Mendeleev's table of elements were really clever because they <u>predicted</u> the properties of undiscovered elements. Since then <u>new elements</u> have been found which fit into the gaps left in Mendeleev's table...

The Periodic Table is a Table of All Known Elements

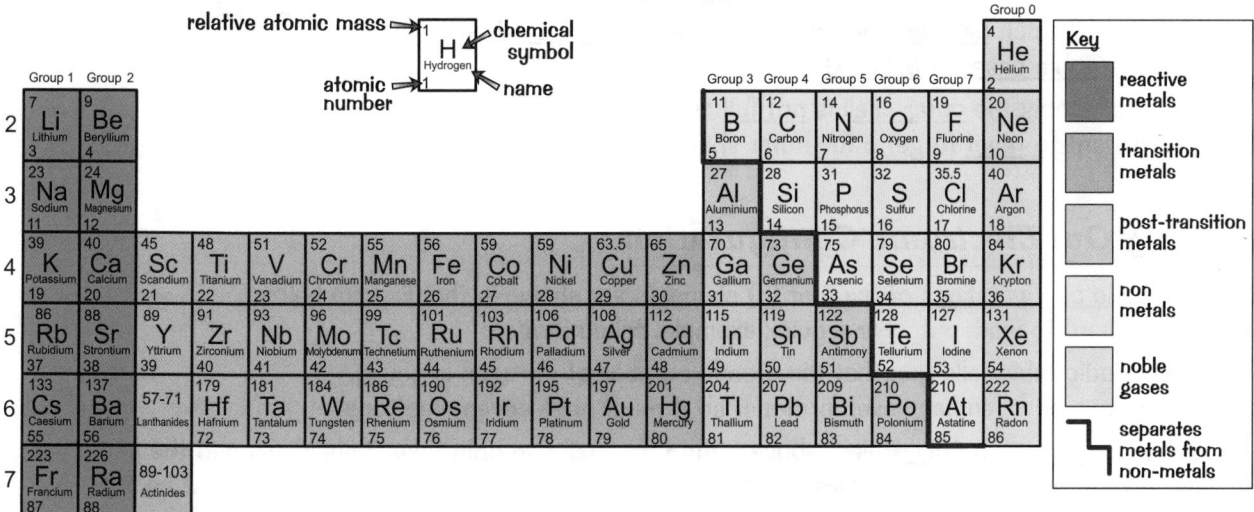

1) We now know there are <u>100ish elements</u> that all materials are made of, with more still being 'discovered'.

2) The <u>modern</u> periodic table shows the elements in order of increasing <u>atomic number</u>.

3) The periodic table is laid out so that elements with <u>similar properties</u> form <u>columns</u>.

4) These <u>vertical columns</u> are called <u>groups</u>.

5) The <u>group</u> to which an element belongs <u>corresponds</u> to the <u>number of electrons</u> it has in its <u>outer shell</u>. (Group 1 elements have 1 outer shell electron, Group 2 elements have 2 outer shell electrons and so on.)

6) Some of the groups have special names. <u>Group 1</u> elements are called <u>alkali metals</u>. <u>Group 7</u> elements are called <u>halogens</u>, and <u>Group 0</u> are called the <u>noble gases</u>.

7) The <u>rows</u> are called <u>periods</u>. The <u>properties</u> of elements <u>change</u> as you go along a period (sometimes quite dramatically).

Elements in a Group Have the Same Number of Outer Electrons

1) The elements in any one <u>group</u> all have the same number of <u>electrons</u> in their <u>outer shell</u>.

2) That's why they have <u>similar properties</u>. And that's why we arrange them in this way.

3) When only a small number of elements were known, the periodic table was made by looking at the <u>properties</u> of the elements and arranging them in groups — the same groups that they are in today.

4) This idea is <u>extremely important</u> to chemistry — so make sure you understand it.

> The properties of the elements depend on the <u>number of electrons</u> they have.
> <u>Atomic number</u> is therefore very significant because it is equal to the number of electrons each atom has.
>
> But it's the number of electrons in the <u>outer shell</u> which is the really important thing.

These jokes are tested for funniness — periodically...

You can use your old mate the periodic table to make predictions about how reactions will occur. How neat is that?

Q1   Based on its position in the periodic table, would you expect the chemical properties of potassium to be more similar to those of sodium or calcium? Explain your answer.   [2 marks]

Electron Shells

Like snails, electrons live in shells. Unlike snails, electrons won't nibble on your petunias...

Electron Shell Rules:

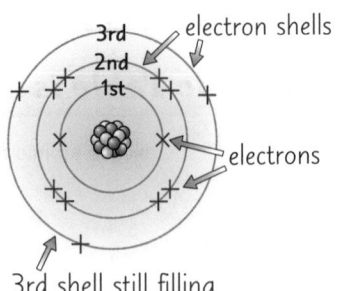

The lowest energy levels are the ones closest to the nucleus.

1) Electrons always occupy shells (sometimes called energy levels).
2) The lowest energy levels are always filled first.
3) Only a certain number of electrons are allowed in each shell:
   1st shell: 2   2nd shell: 8   3rd shell: 8
4) Atoms are much happier when they have full electron shells — like the noble gases in Group 0.
5) In most atoms the outer shell is not full and this makes the atom want to react to get a full outer shell.

3rd shell still filling

Working Out Electronic Configurations

The electronic configurations of the first 20 elements are shown in the diagram below.
They're not hard to work out. For a quick example, take nitrogen:

1) The periodic table tells you that the atomic number of nitrogen is seven.
   That means nitrogen has seven protons, so it must have seven electrons.
2) Follow the 'Electron Shell Rules' above. The first shell can only take 2 electrons and the second shell can take a maximum of 8 electrons. So the electronic configuration of nitrogen must be 2.5.

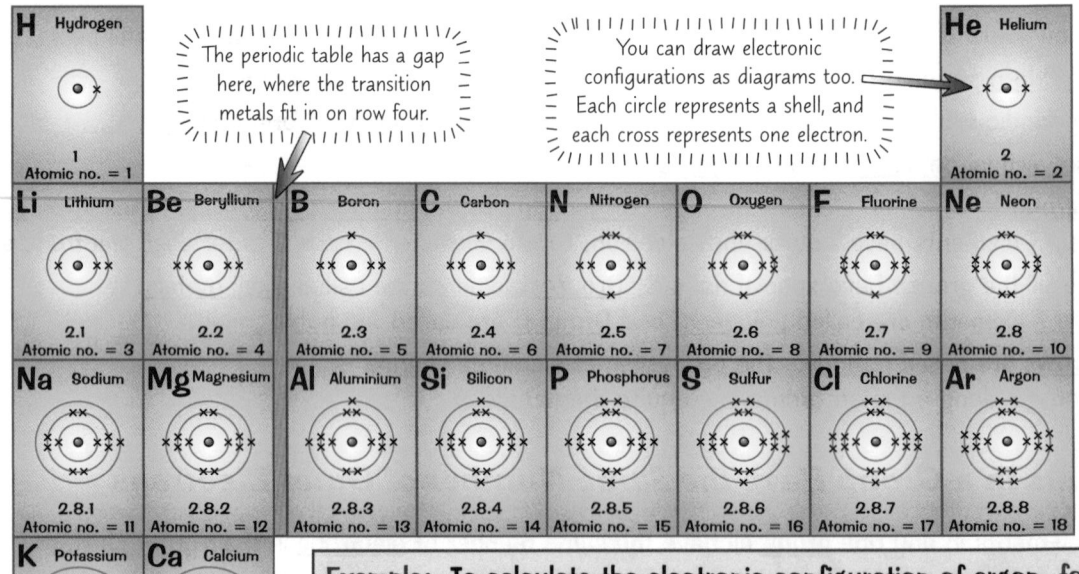

The periodic table has a gap here, where the transition metals fit in on row four.

You can draw electronic configurations as diagrams too. Each circle represents a shell, and each cross represents one electron.

Example: To calculate the electronic configuration of argon, follow the rules. It's got 18 protons, so it must have 18 electrons. The first shell must have 2 electrons, the second shell must have 8, and so the third shell must have 8 as well. It's as easy as 2.8.8.

You can also work out the electronic configuration of an element from its period and group.

- The number of shells which contain electrons is the same as the period of the element.
- The group number tells you how many electrons occupy the outer shell of the element.

Example: Sodium is in period 3, so it has 3 shells occupied. The first two shells must be full (2.8). It's in Group 1, so it has 1 electron in its outer shell. So its electronic configuration is 2.8.1.

The electronic configuration of the fifth element — it's a bit boron...

Electronic configurations may seem a bit complicated at first but once you learn the rules, it's a piece of cake.

Q1   Give the electronic configuration of aluminium (atomic number = 13).   [1 mark]

More on the Periodic Table

Remember that big ol' periodic table back on page 13. Well there's more about it on this page here. It has all the elements in a nice logical order, which makes it great for spotting trends. Honest.

The Elements can be Classified as Metals or Non-Metals

The periodic table can be split into two parts — the metals are on one side and the non-metals are on the other.

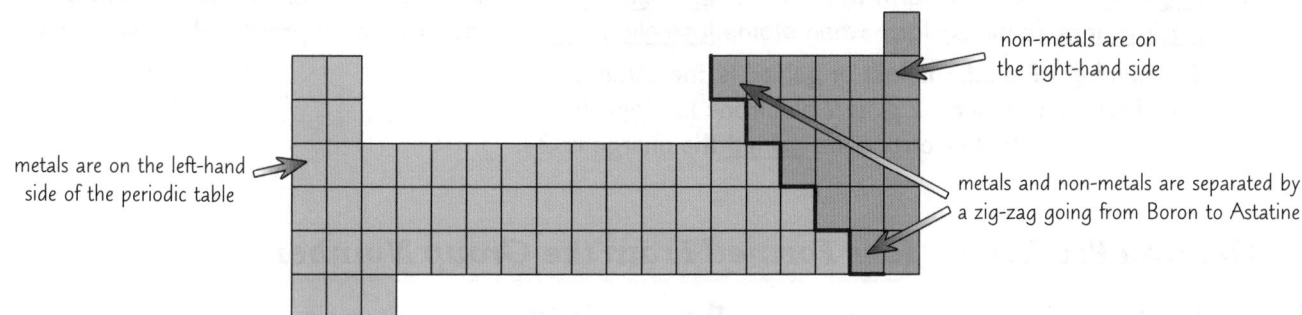

metals are on the left-hand side of the periodic table

non-metals are on the right-hand side

metals and non-metals are separated by a zig-zag going from Boron to Astatine

Metals

1) The elements on the left of the zigzag are all classified as metals.

2) Metals conduct electricity because they allow charge to pass through them easily.

3) Metal oxides are basic.
This means they will neutralise acids. Metal oxides which dissolve will form solutions with a pH of more than 7.

Non-metals

1) The elements on the right of the zigzag are all classified as non-metals.

2) Non-metals are poor conductors of electricity.

3) Non-metal oxides are acidic. This means that they will neutralise bases. They dissolve in water to form solutions with a pH of less than 7.

You can read all about pH on page 46.

Group 0 Elements are All Inert, Colourless Gases

1) Group 0 elements are called the noble gases and include the elements helium, neon and argon (plus a few others).

2) They are inert — this means they don't react with much at all.

3) The reason for this is that they have a full outer shell of electrons. This means they're not desperate to give up or gain electrons. (Atoms are most stable when they have full outer shells — see the previous page for more on electron shells.)

He's always been a bit of a loner...

Because they are inert, noble gases exist as single atoms. They don't go around in pairs like in oxygen (O_2) or hydrogen (H_2).

	Group 0
	4 **He** Helium 2

Group 6	Group 7	
O	F	20 **Ne** Neon 10
S	Cl	40 **Ar** Argon 18
Se	Br	84 **Kr** Krypton 36
Te	I	131 **Xe** Xenon 54
Po	At	222 **Rn** Radon 86

What do you do when all the good chemistry jokes Argon?

The noble gases might seem a bit dull, given how unreactive they are, but they're not so bad. They'd be pretty good at hide and seek for a start. And what would helium balloon sellers be without them? Deflated — that's what.

Q1   A student is testing the pH of two solutions, A and B. A is a solution of a non-metal oxide and B is a solution of a metal oxide. Suggest which solution will have a pH of less than 7.   [1 mark]

Q2   Describe and explain the reactivity of the Group 0 elements.   [2 marks]

Ionic Bonding

Some atoms are keen on getting rid of some of their <u>electrons</u>. Others want more. That's life. And <u>ions</u>...

Simple Ions Form When Atoms Lose or Gain Electrons

1) <u>Ions</u> are <u>charged</u> particles — they can be <u>single atoms</u> (e.g. Na^+) or <u>groups of atoms</u> (e.g. NO_3^-).

2) When <u>atoms</u> lose or gain electrons to form ions, all they're trying to do is get a <u>full outer shell</u> (also called a "<u>stable electronic structure</u>"). Atoms with full outer shells are very <u>stable</u>.

3) <u>Negative ions</u> (anions) form when atoms <u>gain electrons</u> — they have more electrons than protons. <u>Positive ions</u> (cations) form when atoms <u>lose electrons</u> — they have more protons than electrons.

4) The <u>number</u> of electrons lost or gained is the same as the <u>charge</u> on the ion. E.g. If 2 electrons are <u>lost</u> the charge is 2+. If 3 electrons are <u>gained</u> the charge is 3–.

You calculate the number of protons and neutrons in an ion in the same way as for an atom (see page 6).

You Can Predict the Ions Formed From the Group Number

1) <u>Group 1, 2 and 3 elements</u> are <u>metals</u>. They <u>lose</u> electrons to form <u>positive ions</u>.

2) <u>Group 5, 6 and 7 elements</u> are <u>non-metals</u>. They <u>gain</u> electrons to form <u>negative ions</u>.

3) Elements in the same <u>group</u> all have the same number of <u>outer electrons</u>. So they have to <u>lose or gain</u> the same number to get a full outer shell. And this means that they form ions with the <u>same charge</u>.

4) You <u>don't</u> have to <u>remember</u> what ions <u>most elements</u> form — nope, you just look at the periodic table.

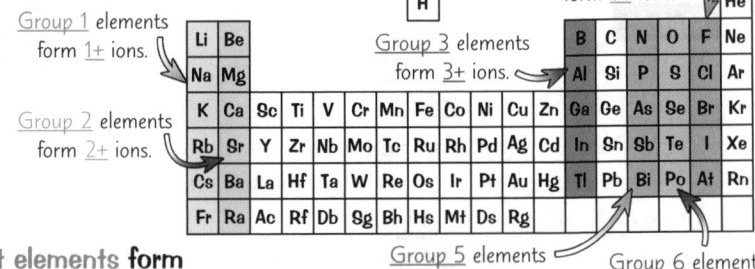

Group 1 elements form <u>1+</u> ions.
Group 2 elements form <u>2+</u> ions.
Group 3 elements form <u>3+</u> ions.
Group 5 elements form <u>3–</u> ions.
Group 6 elements form <u>2–</u> ions.
Group 7 elements form <u>1–</u> ions.

5) Here are some trickier ions that you just have to <u>learn</u>:

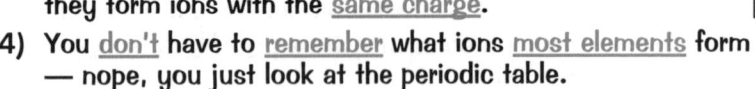

| Ag^+ | Fe^{2+} | Pb^{2+} | Hydrogen: H^+ | Ammonium: NH_4^+ | Nitrate: NO_3^- |
| Cu^{2+} | Fe^{3+} | Zn^{2+} | Hydroxide: OH^- | Carbonate: CO_3^{2-} | Sulfate: SO_4^{2-} |

Ionic Bonding — Transfer of Electrons

1) When a <u>metal</u> and a <u>non-metal</u> react together, such as when Group 1 metals react with Group 7 elements, the <u>metal atom loses</u> electrons to form a <u>positive ion</u> (cation) and the <u>non-metal gains these electrons</u> to form a <u>negative ion</u> (anion).

2) These oppositely charged ions are <u>strongly attracted</u> to one another by <u>electrostatic attractions</u>. This attraction is called an <u>ionic bond</u>.

3) The reaction of sodium and chlorine is a <u>classic case</u> of ionic bonding:

The <u>sodium</u> atom <u>gives up</u> its <u>outer electron</u> and becomes an <u>Na+</u> ion.

The <u>chlorine</u> atom <u>picks up</u> the <u>spare electron</u> and becomes a <u>Cl−</u> ion.

I've got my ion you...

Don't forget about the ions in the green box above. You can't use the periodic table to work out the charges on these, like you can with the elements in Groups 1-3 and 5-7. You just need to learn them.

Q1 State the charge on the following ions:
    a) ammonium, NH_4 b) sulfate, SO_4 c) nitrate, NO_3 [3 marks]

Q2 Describe, in terms of electron transfer, how sodium and chlorine react to form sodium chloride.   [3 marks]

Ionic Compounds

Make sure you've really got your head around the idea of ionic bonding before you start on this page.

You Can Work Out the Formula of an Ionic Compound

1) Ionic compounds are made up of a <u>positively charged</u> part and a <u>negatively charged</u> part.

2) The <u>overall charge</u> of <u>any ionic compound</u> is <u>zero</u>. So all the <u>negative charges</u> in the compound must <u>balance</u> all the <u>positive charges</u>.

3) You can use the charges on the <u>individual ions</u> present to work out the formula for the ionic compound.

> <u>Example</u>: What is the chemical formula of calcium nitrate?
> 1) Write out the <u>formulas</u> of the calcium and nitrate ions: Ca^{2+}, NO_3^-
> 2) Work out the <u>ratio</u> of Ca : NO_3 that gives an <u>overall neutral charge</u> — you'd need 2 lots of NO_3^- to balance out the 2+ charge on Ca^{2+}. So the formula would be $Ca(NO_3)_2$.

The brackets show you need two of the whole nitrate ion.

Ionic Compounds All Form in a Similar Way

You can use '<u>dot and cross</u>' diagrams to show what happens to the electrons when <u>ionic bonding</u> happens:

In these examples, the dots represent the electrons from one of the atoms and the crosses represent the electrons from the other (all electrons are really identical, but this is a good way of following their movement).

<u>Sodium Chloride (NaCl)</u>

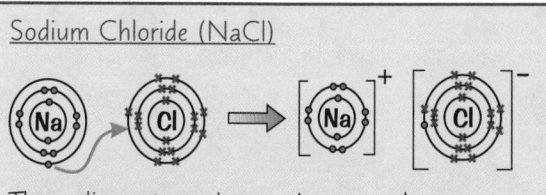

The <u>sodium</u> atom gives up its outer electron, becoming an Na^+ ion. The <u>chlorine</u> atom picks up the electron, becoming a <u>Cl⁻</u> (<u>chloride</u>) ion.

<u>Aluminium Chloride (AlCl₃)</u>

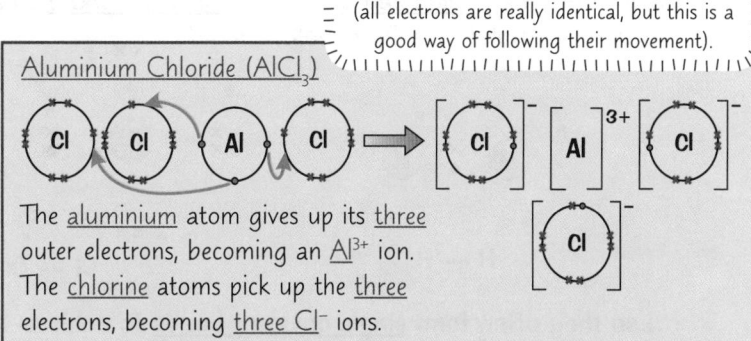

The <u>aluminium</u> atom gives up its <u>three</u> outer electrons, becoming an Al^{3+} ion. The <u>chlorine</u> atoms pick up the <u>three</u> electrons, becoming <u>three Cl⁻</u> ions.

<u>Magnesium Oxide (MgO)</u>

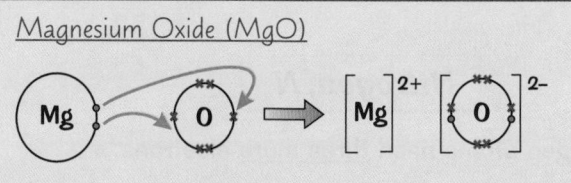

The <u>magnesium</u> atom gives up its <u>two</u> outer electrons, forming an Mg^{2+} ion. The <u>oxygen</u> atom gains the electrons, becoming an O^{2-} (<u>oxide</u>) ion.

<u>Sodium Oxide (Na₂O)</u>

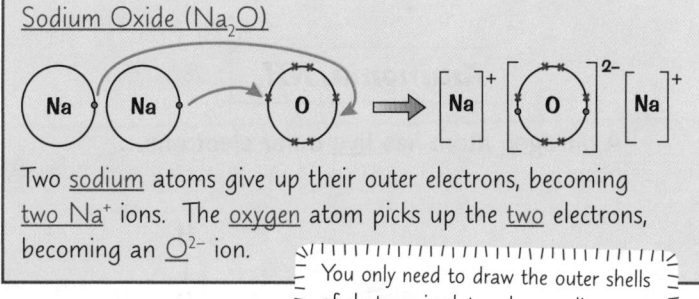

Two <u>sodium</u> atoms give up their outer electrons, becoming <u>two Na⁺</u> ions. The <u>oxygen</u> atom picks up the <u>two</u> electrons, becoming an O^{2-} ion.

You only need to draw the outer shells of electrons in dot and cross diagrams.

Notice that <u>all</u> the atoms end up with <u>full outer shells</u> as a result of this giving and taking of electrons.

Ionic Compounds Have a Lattice Structure

1) Compounds with <u>ionic bonding</u> always have <u>giant ionic structures</u>.

2) The ions are held together in a <u>closely packed</u> 3D lattice arrangement by the attraction between oppositely charged ions.

3) The electrostatic attraction between oppositely charged ions is <u>very strong</u>. Because <u>a lot of energy</u> is needed to overcome the strong attraction, ionic compounds have <u>high melting</u> and <u>boiling points</u>.

4) Ionic compounds are <u>not</u> electrical <u>conductors</u> when they are <u>solid</u>. But if you <u>melt them</u>, or <u>dissolve</u> them in <u>water</u>, they are able to <u>conduct electricity</u>.

Giant ionic lattices — all over your chips...

Make sure you know the properties of ionic compounds inside out and back to front. They may crop up in the exam.

Q1   Explain why calcium chloride, an ionic compound, has a high melting point.   [1 mark]

Covalent Bonding

Ionic bonding (see page 16) isn't the only kind of bonding you need to know about — there's <u>covalent bonding</u> too. This is where atoms <u>share electrons</u> with each other so that they've got <u>full outer shells</u>.

A Covalent Bond is a Shared Pair of Electrons

1) Sometimes atoms prefer to make <u>covalent bonds</u> by <u>sharing</u> pairs of electrons with other atoms.

2) This way <u>both</u> atoms feel that they have a <u>full outer shell</u>, and that makes them very stable.

3) Each <u>covalent bond</u> provides one <u>extra</u> shared electron for each atom.

4) Each atom involved has to make <u>enough</u> covalent bonds to <u>fill up</u> its outer shell.

5) In covalent bonding, there's a strong <u>electrostatic attraction</u> between the negatively charged <u>shared electrons</u> (the bonding pair) and the positively charged <u>nuclei</u> of the atoms involved.

<u>Learn</u> these <u>important</u> examples:

An electrostatic attraction is when two (or more) oppositely charged particles are attracted to each other.

Hydrogen, H_2

Hydrogen atoms have just one electron. They <u>only need one</u> more to complete the first shell...

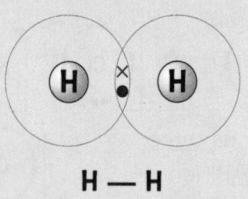

H — H

...so they often form <u>single covalent bonds</u> to achieve this.

Chlorine, Cl_2

...chlorine atoms also need <u>only one more</u> electron...

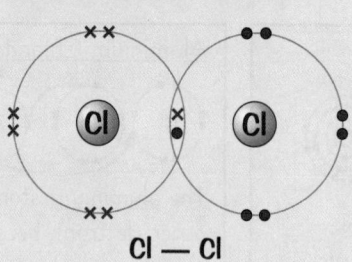

Cl — Cl

Hydrogen Chloride, HCl

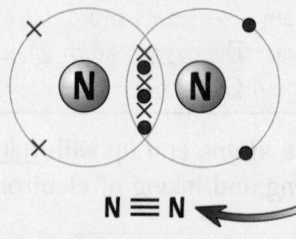

H — Cl

This is very similar to H_2 and Cl_2. Again, both atoms <u>only need one more electron</u> to complete their outer shells.

Ammonia, NH_3

A nitrogen atom has <u>five</u> outer electrons...

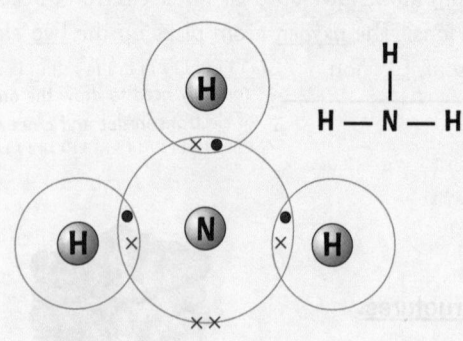

```
      H
      |
  H — N — H
```

...so it needs to form <u>three covalent bonds</u> with hydrogen atoms to make up the extra <u>three</u> electrons needed to fill its outer shell.

Nitrogen, N_2

Nitrogen atoms need <u>three more</u> electrons...

N ≡ N

This is the displayed formula of a molecule of nitrogen (see page 67 for more).

...so <u>two nitrogen atoms</u> share <u>three pairs of electrons</u> to fill their outer shells. This creates a <u>triple bond</u>.

When you've drawn a dot and cross diagram, it's a good idea to count up the number of electrons, just to double-check you've got the right number in the outer shell.

Know any good jokes about covalent bonding? Please, do share...

There's another page of covalent bonding diagrams to come, but make sure you can draw the dot and cross diagrams for the covalent compounds on this page first.

Q1 How many electrons are shared in a single covalent bond? [1 mark]

Q2 Draw a dot and cross diagram to show bonding in a molecule of ammonia (NH_3). [2 marks]

More on Covalent Bonding

Oxygen atoms have six outer electrons and need two more to complete their outer shell.

Water, H₂O
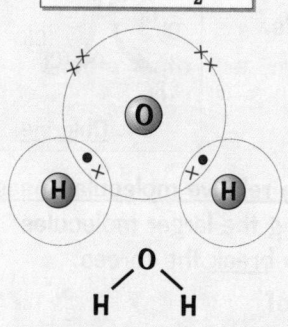

In water molecules, the oxygen shares a pair of electrons with two H atoms to form two single covalent bonds.

Oxygen, O₂
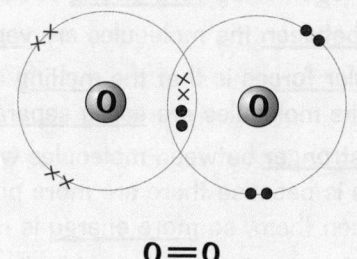

O=O

In oxygen gas one oxygen atom shares two pairs of electrons with another to form a double covalent bond.

Carbon Dioxide, CO₂
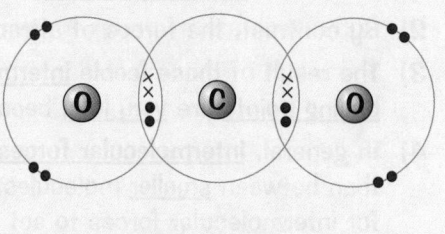

O=C=O

In carbon dioxide two oxygen atoms share two pairs of electrons with a carbon atom to form two double covalent bonds.

Methane, CH₄
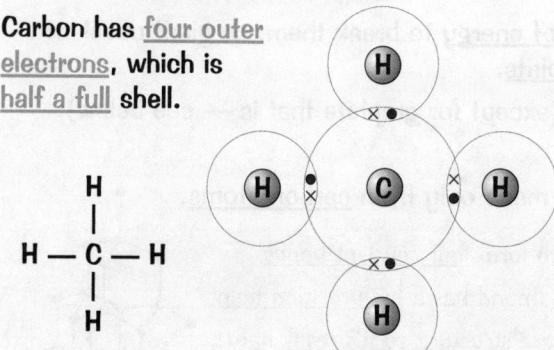

Carbon has four outer electrons, which is half a full shell.

It forms four covalent bonds with hydrogen atoms to fill up its outer shell.

Ethane, C₂H₆
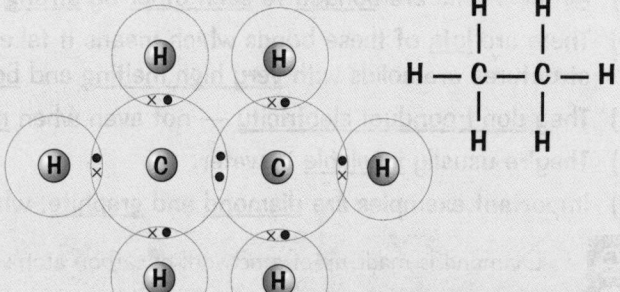

In ethane, 6 hydrogen atoms each share their only electron with one of two carbon atoms. The two carbon atoms then share their last electrons with each other in a single covalent bond.

Chloromethane, CH₃Cl
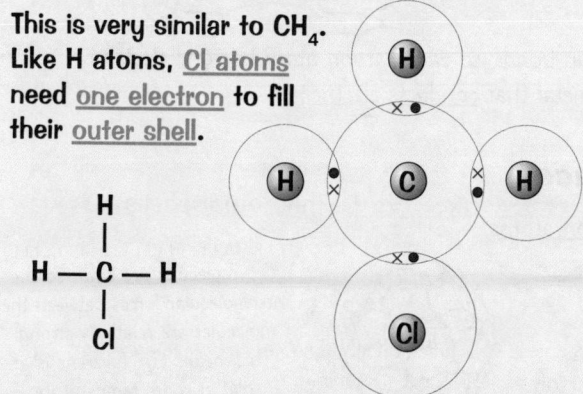

This is very similar to CH₄. Like H atoms, Cl atoms need one electron to fill their outer shell.

Carbon forms four covalent bonds — three with hydrogen atoms and one with a chlorine atom.

Ethene, C₂H₄
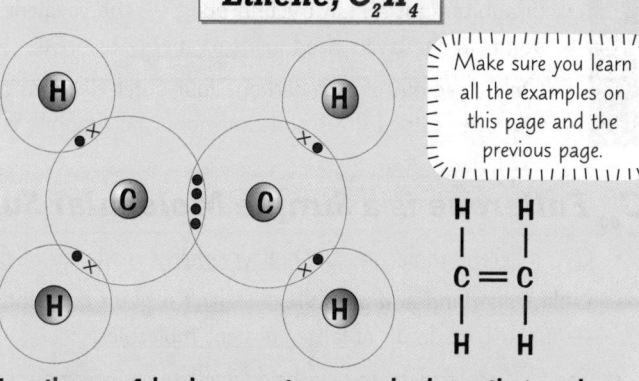

Make sure you learn all the examples on this page and the previous page.

In ethene, 4 hydrogen atoms each share their only electron with one of two carbon atoms. The two carbon atoms then share their last two electrons with each other to form a carbon-carbon double bond.

Double bonds — now that's just being greedy...

So a single bond is one pair of shared electrons, a double bond is two pairs and a triple bond is three pairs. Amazing eh?

Q1   Draw dot and cross diagrams to represent the bonding in: a) ethane (C₂H₆)   b) ethene (C₂H₄).   [4 marks]

Covalent Substances

Substances containing <u>covalent bonds</u> can be <u>simple molecules</u> or <u>giant structures</u>.

Simple Molecular Substances

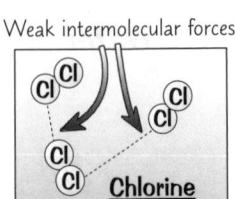

Weak intermolecular forces

Chlorine

1) The atoms <u>within a molecule</u> are held together by <u>very strong</u> covalent bonds.

2) By contrast, the forces of attraction <u>between</u> the molecules are <u>very weak</u>.

3) The result of these feeble <u>intermolecular forces</u> is that the <u>melting</u> and <u>boiling points</u> are <u>very low</u>, because the molecules are <u>easily separated</u>.

4) In general, <u>intermolecular forces</u> are <u>stronger</u> between molecules with a <u>high relative molecular mass</u> (M_r) than between <u>smaller</u> molecules. This is because there are more points along the larger molecules for intermolecular forces to act between them, so <u>more energy</u> is needed to <u>break</u> the forces.

5) Due to the increasing strength of the forces, the <u>melting</u> and <u>boiling points</u> of simple molecular substances <u>increase</u> as the <u>relative molecular mass increases</u>.

6) Most molecular substances are <u>gases or liquids</u> at room temperature. You can usually spot one just by its <u>physical state</u> — it'll either be a <u>liquid</u> or <u>gas</u> or an <u>easily melted solid</u>.

> The M_r of a molecule is a measure of how big it is.

Giant Covalent Structures

1) These are similar to giant ionic structures (p.17) except that there are <u>no charged ions</u>.

2) <u>All</u> the atoms are <u>bonded</u> to <u>each other</u> by <u>strong</u> covalent bonds.

3) There are <u>lots</u> of these bonds which means it takes a <u>lot of energy</u> to break them, so giant covalent structures are solids with <u>very high melting</u> and <u>boiling points</u>.

4) They <u>don't conduct electricity</u> — not even when <u>molten</u> (except for graphite that is — see below).

5) They're usually <u>insoluble</u> in water.

6) Important examples are <u>diamond</u> and <u>graphite</u>, which are made only from <u>carbon atoms</u>.

DIAMOND

- Diamond is made up of a network of carbon atoms that each form <u>four covalent bonds</u>.
- The <u>strong covalent bonds</u> take lots of energy to break, so diamond has a <u>high melting point</u>.
- The strong covalent bonds hold the atoms in a very <u>rigid lattice structure</u>, so it's <u>really hard</u>.
- It <u>doesn't conduct electricity</u> because it has <u>no free electrons</u> or <u>ions</u>.

GRAPHITE

- In graphite, each carbon atom only forms <u>three covalent bonds</u>, creating <u>layers</u> of <u>carbon atoms</u>. The layers are only held together <u>weakly</u> by <u>intermolecular forces</u>, so are free to slide over each other. This makes graphite <u>soft</u> and <u>slippery</u>.
- Graphite's got a <u>high melting point</u> — the covalent bonds in the layers need <u>loads of energy</u> to break.
- Only <u>three</u> out of each carbon's four outer electrons are used in bonds, so each carbon atom has <u>one</u> electron that's <u>delocalised</u> (free) and can move. So graphite is a non-metal that <u>conducts electricity</u>.

C_{60} Fullerene is a Simple Molecular Substance

- <u>C_{60} fullerene</u> molecules are <u>hollow spheres</u> made up of <u>60 carbon atoms</u>.
- Unlike diamond and graphite, C_{60} <u>isn't</u> a giant covalent structure — it's just made up of <u>large covalent molecules</u>.
- The C_{60} molecules are only held together by <u>intermolecular forces</u> and so they can <u>slide</u> over each other. This means the material is <u>soft</u>.
- Like graphite, each carbon in C_{60} fullerene has <u>one delocalised electron</u>. However, the electrons can't move <u>between</u> the molecules, so C_{60} fullerene is a <u>poor conductor</u> of <u>electricity</u>.

> C_{60} molecules are large, so the intermolecular forces between the molecules are relatively strong. This means C_{60} fullerene is a solid at room temperature.

May the intermolecular forces be with you...

Make sure you know how the structures of diamond, graphite and C_{60} fullerene determine their physical properties.

Q1   Explain why graphite can conduct electricity, but diamond cannot.   [2 marks]

Electrical Conductivity and Metals

Metals are pretty good conductors of electricity — it's all about the <u>movement</u> of electrons or ions.

Electric Current is a Flow of Electrons or Ions

1) <u>Electrons</u> have a <u>negative</u> charge. <u>Ions</u> can have either a <u>negative</u> or a <u>positive</u> charge.

2) When electrons or ions <u>move</u>, they can cause the material they're in to <u>conduct electricity</u>.

3) The electric current is the <u>flow</u> of the electrons or ions.

Ionic Compounds Only Conduct Electricity when Molten or in Solution

1) Ionic compounds are made of a <u>lattice</u> of <u>positive and negative ions</u> (more on this on pages 16-17).

2) <u>Solid</u> ionic compounds <u>don't</u> conduct electricity because the ions <u>aren't</u> able to move around.

3) When an ionic compound is <u>dissolved</u> the ions separate and are <u>able to move</u> in the <u>solution</u>. This means that the compound will <u>conduct electricity</u>.

4) When an ionic compound <u>melts</u>, the ions are also <u>able to move</u> so the compound can <u>conduct electricity</u>.

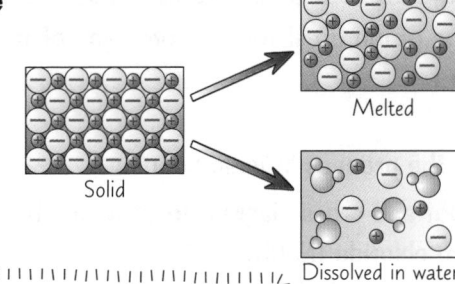

Solid

Melted

Dissolved in water

> Covalent compounds don't have any charged particles that are able to move, so they can't conduct electricity (except for graphite — see previous page.)

Metals are Held Together by Metallic Bonding

1) Metals have a <u>giant structure</u> of <u>positive ions</u> surrounded by a <u>sea of delocalised electrons</u>.

2) The <u>electrostatic attractions</u> between the positive ions and the electrons is called <u>metallic bonding</u>.

3) It's this metallic bonding which gives metals their <u>properties</u>.

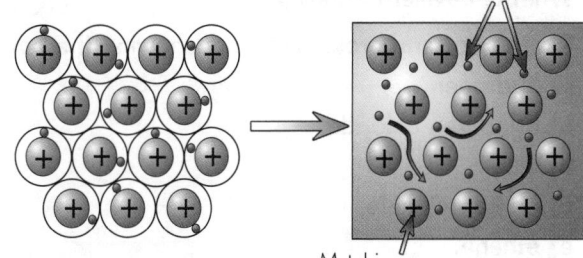

Delocalised electrons

Metal ions

Metals are Good Conductors of Electricity and Heat

The <u>delocalised electrons</u> are able to <u>move</u> through the structure. This means metals can conduct <u>electricity</u>. The movement of electrons also means <u>energy</u> can be transferred quickly through the material, so metals are good conductors of <u>heat</u>.

> Delocalised electrons are also known as free electrons.

Most Metals are Malleable

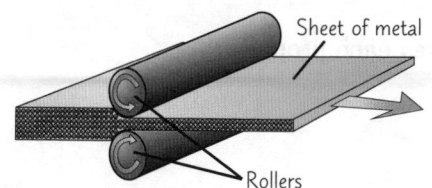

Sheet of metal

Rollers

The layers of ions in a metal can <u>slide</u> over each other, making metals <u>malleable</u> — this means that they can be <u>hammered</u> or <u>rolled</u> into <u>flat sheets</u>.

I saw a metal on the bus once — he was the conductor...

If your knowledge of metals is still feeling a bit delocalised, the questions below will help...

Q1   Explain why the structure of a metal allows it to be rolled into flat sheets.   [1 mark]

Q2   Copper is a metallic element. State what property of copper makes it suitable for using in electrical circuits and explain why it has this property.   [2 marks]

Paper 2

P2

Revision Questions for Section 2

And that's it for <u>Section 2</u>. If I had to pick a favourite page, it would be all of them.

- Try these questions and <u>tick off each one</u> when you <u>get it right</u>.
- When you've done <u>all the questions</u> under a heading and are <u>completely happy</u> with it, tick it off.

<u>The Periodic Table and Electron Shells (p.13-15)</u> ☑

1) What feature of atoms determines the order of the modern periodic table?
2) How many electrons are in the outer shell of an atom of a Group 7 element?
3) Describe how you would work out the electronic configuration of an atom, given its atomic number.
4) Are the elements in Group 1 metals or non-metals?

<u>Ionic Bonding and Compounds (p.16-17)</u> ☐

5) What type of ion do elements from each of the following groups form?
   a) Group 1
   b) Group 7
6) Describe the process of ionic bonding.
7) Draw a dot and cross diagram to show the bonding in:
   a) sodium chloride (NaCl),
   b) magnesium oxide (MgO).
8) State three properties of ionic compounds.

<u>Covalent Bonding and Compounds (p.18-20)</u> ☑

9) What is covalent bonding?
10) Sketch dot and cross diagrams showing the bonding in molecules of:
    a) hydrogen,
    b) hydrogen chloride,
    c) water,
    d) carbon dioxide,
    e) ethene.
11) a) Describe one property of simple molecular substances.
    b) Explain how the bonding in simple molecular substances causes this property.
12) Explain how the bonding in diamond causes its physical properties.
13) Explain why C_{60} fullerene is a poor conductor of electricity.

<u>Electrical Conductivity and Metals (p.21)</u> ☑

14) Explain why ionic compounds only conduct electricity when molten or in solution.
15) What is metallic bonding?
16) List two properties of metals and explain how metallic structure causes each property.

Balancing Equations

Equations crop up <u>everywhere</u> in chemistry — you can't hide from them. They show you just what's happening in a chemical reaction — what <u>reacts together</u> and what's <u>formed</u>.

Equations Show the Reactants and Products of a Reaction

A chemical reaction can be described as the process of going from <u>reactants</u> to <u>products</u>. You can write <u>word equations</u> or <u>symbol equations</u> to show any chemical reaction.

> E.g. <u>magnesium</u> reacts with <u>oxygen</u> to produce <u>magnesium oxide</u>:
>
> Word equation: magnesium + oxygen → magnesium oxide
>
> Symbol equation: $2Mg$ + O_2 → $2MgO$

See page 2 for more on states.

Look out for <u>state symbols</u> in equations — they tell you what <u>physical state</u> the reactants and products are in:

| (s) — Solid | (l) — Liquid | (g) — Gas | (aq) — Aqueous (dissolved in water) |

Here's the example including state symbols: $2Mg(s) + O_2(g) \rightarrow 2MgO(s)$

So, this is solid magnesium reacting with oxygen gas to make solid magnesium oxide.

Symbol Equations Need to be Balanced

E=mc²

1) There must always be the <u>same</u> number of atoms of each element on <u>both sides</u> of the equation — atoms can't just <u>disappear</u>.

2) You <u>balance</u> the equation by putting numbers <u>in front</u> of the formulas where needed. Take this equation for reacting sulfuric acid with sodium hydroxide:

$$H_2SO_4 + NaOH \rightarrow Na_2SO_4 + H_2O$$

3) The <u>formulas</u> are all correct but the numbers of some atoms <u>don't match up</u> on both sides.

4) You <u>can't change formulas</u> like H_2SO_4 to H_2SO_5. You can only put numbers <u>in front of them</u>.

5) The more you <u>practise</u>, the <u>quicker</u> you get, but all you do is this:

- Find an element that <u>doesn't balance</u> and <u>pencil in a number</u> to try and sort it out.
- <u>See where it gets you</u>. It may create <u>another imbalance</u>, but if so, pencil in <u>another number</u> and see where that gets you.
- Carry on chasing <u>unbalanced</u> elements and it'll <u>sort itself out</u> pretty quickly.

> In the equation above you soon notice we're short of H atoms on the RHS (right-hand side).
>
> 1) The only thing you can do about that is make it $2H_2O$ instead of just H_2O:
>
> $$H_2SO_4 + NaOH \rightarrow Na_2SO_4 + 2H_2O$$
>
> 2) But that now gives too many H atoms and O atoms on the RHS, so to balance that up you could try putting a 2 in front of the NaOH on the LHS (left-hand side):
>
> $$H_2SO_4 + 2NaOH \rightarrow Na_2SO_4 + 2H_2O$$
>
> *Putting a 2 in front of the NaOH has sorted out the Na atoms too.*
>
> 3) And suddenly there it is. <u>Everything balances</u>.

Revision is all about getting the balance right...

Balancing equations is all about practice. Once you have a few goes you'll see it's much less scary than it seemed before you took on, challenged and defeated this page. Go and grab some chemistry glory.

Q1   Balance the equation: $Fe + Cl_2 \rightarrow FeCl_3$ [1 mark]

Q2   Hydrogen and oxygen molecules are formed in a reaction where water splits apart.
        For this reaction: a) State the word equation.   b) Give a balanced symbol equation.   [3 marks]

Relative Formula Mass

Time for some <u>maths</u>. "But this is <u>chemistry</u>, not maths," I hear you cry. "Tough cookies," I reply.

Relative Formula Mass, M_r

If you have a compound like $MgCl_2$ then it has a <u>relative formula mass</u>, M_r, which is just all the relative atomic masses (A_r) of the atoms it contains <u>added together</u>.

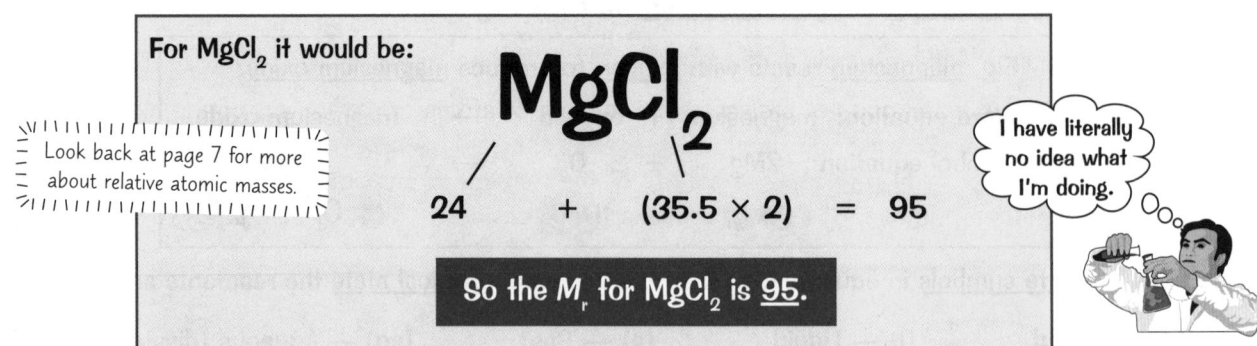

For $MgCl_2$ it would be:

$$MgCl_2$$

Look back at page 7 for more about relative atomic masses.

$$24 \quad + \quad (35.5 \times 2) \quad = \quad 95$$

I have literally no idea what I'm doing.

So the M_r for $MgCl_2$ is <u>95</u>.

You can easily get the A_r for any element from the <u>periodic table</u>.
In the exam you'll be given a periodic table so you can look them up.

I'll tell you what, since it's nearly Christmas I'll run through a couple more examples for you:

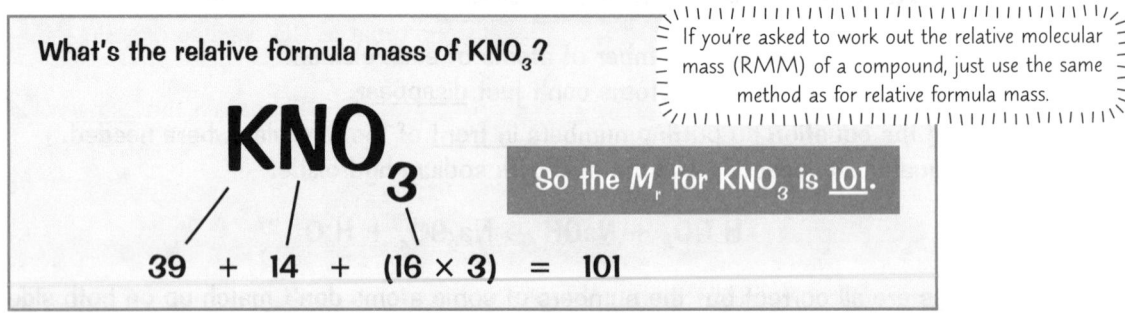

What's the relative formula mass of KNO_3?

If you're asked to work out the relative molecular mass (RMM) of a compound, just use the same method as for relative formula mass.

$$KNO_3$$

So the M_r for KNO_3 is <u>101</u>.

$$39 \quad + \quad 14 \quad + \quad (16 \times 3) \quad = \quad 101$$

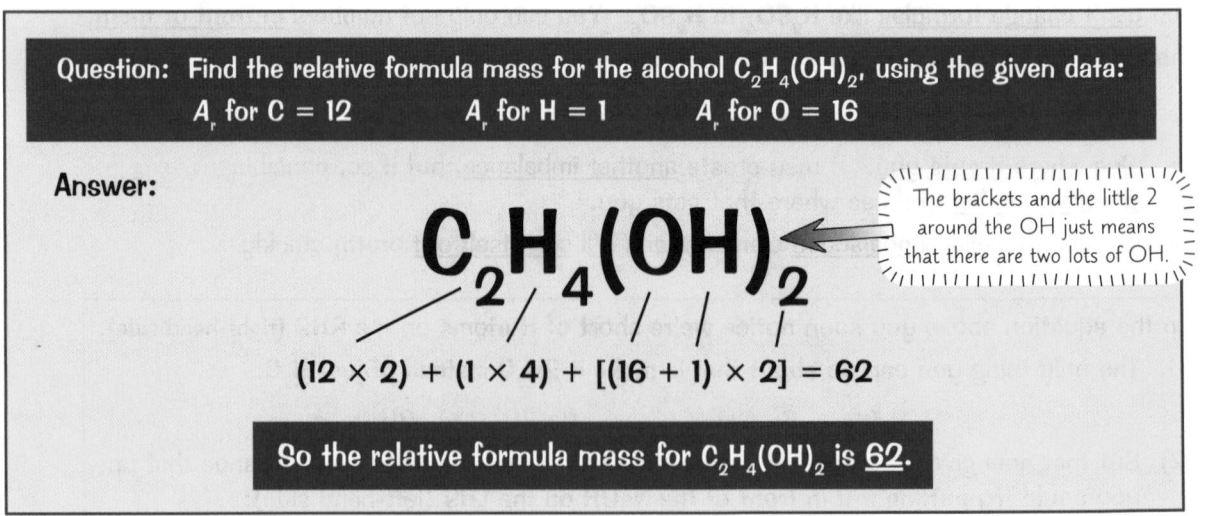

Question: Find the relative formula mass for the alcohol $C_2H_4(OH)_2$, using the given data:
A_r for C = 12 A_r for H = 1 A_r for O = 16

Answer:

$$C_2H_4(OH)_2$$

The brackets and the little 2 around the OH just means that there are two lots of OH.

$$(12 \times 2) + (1 \times 4) + [(16 + 1) \times 2] = 62$$

So the relative formula mass for $C_2H_4(OH)_2$ is <u>62</u>.

And that's all it is. A big fancy name like <u>relative formula mass</u> and all it means is "<u>add up all the mass numbers</u>". What a swizz, eh? You'd have thought it'd be something a bit juicier than that, wouldn't you. Still, that's life — it's all a big disappointment in the end. Sigh.

This page is a relative masterpiece...

This stuff comes up a fair bit in chemistry, so make sure you've got to grips with it by doing loads of practice questions. Start with these. Use the periodic table on page 94 to find the A_r values you need.

Q1   Calculate the relative formula mass of:
      a) ethanol, C_2H_5OH [1 mark]
      b) aniline, $C_6H_5NH_2$ [1 mark]

Moles

The mole might seem a bit confusing. I think it's the word that puts people off. But it's not that hard really...

"The Mole" is Simply the Unit for the Amount of a Substance

1) Just like "a million" is this many: 1 000 000; or "a billion" is this many: 1 000 000 000, so "a mole" is this many: <u>602 300 000 000 000 000 000 000</u> or <u>6.023×10^{23}</u>.

2) And that's <u>all</u> it is. Just a <u>number</u>. The burning question, of course, is why is it such a silly long one like that, and with a six at the front?

3) The answer is that when you get precisely that number of atoms or molecules, of any element or compound, then, conveniently, they weigh exactly the <u>same</u> number of grams as the <u>relative atomic mass</u>, A_r (or <u>relative formula mass</u>, M_r) of the element or compound. This is arranged on purpose, of course, to make things easier.

> One mole of atoms or molecules of any substance will have a mass in grams equal to the relative particle mass (A_r or M_r) for that substance.

EXAMPLES

Carbon has an A_r of 12.	So one mole of carbon weighs exactly 12 g.
Nitrogen gas, N_2, has an M_r of 28 (2×14).	So one mole of N_2 weighs exactly 28 g.
Carbon dioxide, CO_2, has an M_r of 44.	So one mole of CO_2 weighs exactly 44 g.

4) This means that 12 g of carbon, or 28 g of N_2, or 44 g of CO_2, all contain the <u>same number of particles</u>, namely <u>one mole</u> or 6.023×10^{23} atoms or molecules.

5) The <u>molar mass</u> of a substance is just another way of saying '<u>the mass of one mole</u>'. Molar mass is measured in <u>grams</u> too. E.g. the molar mass of carbon is <u>12 g</u>.

Nice Easy Formula for Finding the Number of Moles in a Given Mass:

$$\text{Number of Moles} = \frac{\text{Mass in g (of element or compound)}}{M_r \ \text{(of element or compound)}}$$

> <u>Example</u>: How many moles are there in 66 g of carbon dioxide?
>
> <u>Method</u>: M_r of $CO_2 = 12 + (16 \times 2) = 44$
> No. of moles = Mass (g) $\div M_r = 66 \div 44 = 1.5$ moles. Easy Peasy.

1) You may need to <u>rearrange</u> the equation to find the mass of a certain number of moles.

2) Putting an equation into a <u>formula triangle</u> makes rearranging equations straightforward. Here's the formula triangle that links moles, mass and relative formula mass.

3) To use a formula triangle, just cover the thing you want to find, and you're left with the expression you need to calculate it. The <u>line</u> through the triangle stands for <u>division</u>.

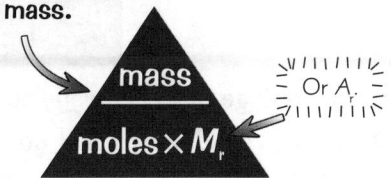

I've got 6.023×10^{23} problems but a mole ain't one...

Moles can definitely be a bit confusing. You need to be able to convert between moles and grams for the exam though — so spend a bit of time getting your head round all this if you need to.

Q1   Calculate the number of moles in 90 g of water. M_r of water = 18.   [1 mark]

Q2   Calculate the mass, in grams, of 2.2 moles of calcium carbonate. M_r of calcium carbonate = 100.   [1 mark]

Calculating Masses in Reactions

These can be kinda scary too, but no need to fear — just grab a brew, relax and enjoy.

You can Calculate the Amount of Product from a Mass of Reactant

You can use a balanced chemical equation to work out the mass of product formed from a given mass of a reactant. Here's how...

Don't worry — these steps should all make sense when you look at the example below.

1) Write out the balanced equation.

2) Work out relative formula masses (M_r) of the reactant and product you're interested in.

3) Find out how many moles there are of the substance you know the mass of.

4) Use the balanced equation to work out how many moles there'll be of the other substance (i.e. how many moles of product will be made by this many moles of reactant).

5) Use the number of moles to calculate the mass.

Example: What mass of magnesium oxide is produced when 60 g of magnesium is burnt in air?

1) Write out the balanced equation: $2Mg + O_2 \rightarrow 2MgO$

2) Work out the relative formula masses of the reactants and products you're interested in:

   Mg: 24   MgO: 24 + 16 = 40

In this reaction, O_2 is in excess. This means that there is more O_2 available to react than there is Mg. So, it's the amount of Mg that determines how much MgO is made.

3) Calculate the number of moles of magnesium in 60 g:

   moles = mass ÷ M_r = 60 ÷ 24 = 2.5

4) Look at the ratio of moles in the equation — 2 moles of Mg react to produce 2 moles of MgO. So 2.5 moles of Mg will react to produce 2.5 moles of MgO.

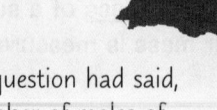

5) Calculate the mass of 2.5 moles of magnesium oxide:

   mass = moles × M_r = 2.5 × 40 = 100

This tells us that 60 g of magnesium will produce 100 g of magnesium oxide. If the question had said, "Find how much magnesium gives 500 g of magnesium oxide", you'd calculate the number of moles of magnesium oxide first, because that's the one you'd have the information about. Got it? Good-O!

The mass of product (in this case magnesium oxide) is called the yield of a reaction. Masses you calculate in this way are called theoretical yields. In practice you never get 100% of the yield, so the amount of product you get will be less than you calculated.

Percentage Yield Compares Actual and Theoretical Yield

The more reactant you start with, the higher the yield will be — that's pretty obvious.
But the percentage yield doesn't depend on the amount of reactants you started with — it's a percentage.

1) The theoretical yield of a reaction can be calculated from the balanced equation (see above).

2) Percentage yield is given by the formula:

$$\text{percentage yield} = \frac{\text{actual yield (grams)}}{\text{theoretical yield (grams)}} \times 100$$

3) Percentage yield is always somewhere between 0 and 100%.

4) A 100% yield means that you got all the product you expected to get.

5) A 0% yield means that no reactants were converted into product, i.e. no product at all was made.

Relative mass — when you go to church with your parents...

A specially organically grown, hand-picked question for you, my dear. Don't say I don't spoil you.

Q1   Chlorine (Cl_2) and potassium bromide (KBr) react according to this equation: $Cl_2 + 2KBr \rightarrow Br_2 + 2KCl$
   a)   Calculate the mass of Br_2 formed when 23.8 g of KBr reacts with an excess of Cl_2.   [4 marks]
   b)   Sam carries out the reaction and obtains a yield of 12.4 g of Br_2. What is the percentage yield?   [2 marks]

Empirical and Molecular Formulae

This sounds a lot worse than it really is. Just follow the same <u>method</u> every time and you'll be laughing.

Finding the Empirical Formula (from Masses or Percentages)

1) The empirical formula gives you the <u>smallest whole number ratio</u> of atoms in a compound.
2) Try this for an easy peasy <u>stepwise method</u> for calculating an empirical formula:

> 1) <u>List all the elements</u> in the compound (there are usually only two or three).
> 2) <u>Underneath them</u>, write their <u>experimental masses</u>.
> 3) Find the number of <u>moles</u> of each element by <u>dividing</u> each mass by the <u>relative atomic mass</u> (A_r) for that particular element.
> 4) Turn the numbers you get into <u>a nice simple ratio</u> by dividing by the <u>smallest</u> number of moles.
> 5) Get the ratio in its <u>simplest whole number form</u> — that's the empirical formula of the compound.

If the amounts of each element are in percentages, just divide each one by the A_r for that element. Then carry on with the method as normal.

Example: In an experiment, some <u>iron oxide</u> powder is reduced to <u>pure metallic iron</u>. Use the following <u>experimental data</u> to find the <u>empirical formula</u> of the iron oxide used.

Mass of empty container	32.0 g
Mass of container + mass of iron oxide	96.0 g
Mass of container + iron	76.8 g

(A_r for iron = 56, A_r for oxygen = 16)

Method:
During the experiment <u>oxygen</u> is <u>lost</u>. The <u>mass of oxygen lost</u> is the difference between the mass of the container and iron oxide and the mass of the container and iron: 96.0 g − 76.8 g = 19.2 g.

The <u>mass of iron made</u> is the difference between the mass of the container with the iron and the mass of the empty container: 76.8 g − 32.0 g = 44.8 g.

1) List the two elements: Fe   O
2) Write in the experimental masses: 44.8   19.2
3) Find the number of moles of each element: 44.8 ÷ 56 = 0.8   19.2 ÷ 16 = 1.2
4) Divide by the smallest number of moles: 0.8 ÷ 0.8 = 1   1.2 ÷ 0.8 = 1.5
5) Multiply to get whole numbers: 1 × 2 = 2   1.5 × 2 = 3

You don't have to multiply if you get whole numbers in step 4.

So the simplest formula is 2 atoms of Fe to 3 atoms of O, i.e. Fe_2O_3. And that's it done.

The Empirical Formula isn't Always the Same as the Molecular Formula

1) The <u>empirical formula</u> of a compound is the <u>simplest</u> formula that tells you the <u>ratio</u> of different elements in the compound.

2) This is different to the <u>molecular formula</u> of a compound, which tells you the <u>actual number</u> of atoms of each element in a single molecule.

3) <u>Molecular formulae</u> are <u>whole-number multiples</u> of empirical formulae.

Simon decided to test out his new moleculars.

Example: A molecule has an empirical formula of $C_4H_3O_2$, and a relative molecular mass of 166. Work out its <u>molecular formula</u>.

Method: 1) Find the <u>mass</u> of the <u>empirical formula</u>: (4 × 12) + (3 × 1) + (2 × 16) = 48 + 3 + 32 = 83 g

2) The relative molecular mass is 166, so there are 166 ÷ 83 = <u>2 empirical units</u> in the molecule.

3) The molecular formula must be the empirical formula × 2, so the molecular formula must be $C_4H_3O_2$ × 2 = $C_8H_6O_4$. So there you go.

The empirical strikes back...

Make sure you read through these examples thoroughly, until you're sure you can follow what's going on.

Q1   A 45.6 g sample of an oxide of nitrogen contains 13.9 g of nitrogen. What is the empirical formula of the nitrogen oxide?   [3 marks]

Finding Formulae Using Experiments

Ever wanted to know how to carry out <u>experiments</u> to determine the <u>empirical formula</u> of a compound? No? Can't say I have either. Unfortunately you need to know how to anyway...

You can find Empirical Formulae using Combustion... PRACTICAL

<u>Combustion</u> happens when a substance <u>reacts</u> with <u>oxygen</u> when it's burned in air.
Here's how you could use <u>combustion</u> to calculate the <u>empirical formula</u> of a metal oxide, e.g. magnesium oxide:

1) Get a <u>crucible</u> and heat it until it's red hot. (This will make sure it's <u>clean</u> and there are no traces of <u>oil or water</u> lying around from a previous experiment.)

2) Leave the crucible to <u>cool</u>, then <u>weigh</u> it, along with its lid.

3) Add some clean <u>magnesium ribbon</u> to the crucible. <u>Reweigh</u> the crucible, lid and magnesium ribbon. The <u>mass of magnesium</u> you're using is this reading minus the initial reading for the mass of the crucible and lid.

4) <u>Heat</u> the crucible containing the magnesium. Put the lid on the crucible so as to <u>stop</u> any bits of solid from <u>escaping</u>, but leave a <u>small gap</u> to allow <u>oxygen</u> to enter the crucible.

5) Heat the crucible strongly for around <u>10 minutes</u>, or until all the magnesium ribbon has turned <u>white</u>.

6) Allow the crucible to <u>cool</u> and <u>reweigh</u> the crucible with the lid and its contents. The <u>mass</u> of <u>magnesium oxide</u> you have is this reading, minus the initial reading for the mass of the crucible and lid.

lid · crucible containing magnesium ribbon · gauze · tripod · **HEAT**

... or using Reduction PRACTICAL

<u>Reduction</u> is the <u>loss</u> of <u>oxygen</u> from a substance (see page 44 for more on reduction).
You can reduce a <u>metal oxide</u> to find out its <u>empirical formula</u>. Here's how you'd do it for copper(II) oxide:

1) Place a rubber <u>bung</u> (with a hole through the middle) into a <u>test tube</u> with a small hole in the end, and <u>weigh</u> them using a mass balance.

2) Take the bung out of the test tube and spread out a small amount of <u>copper(II) oxide</u> in the <u>middle</u> of the tube.

3) Re-insert the bung and <u>weigh</u> the test tube again. Set up the equipment as shown in the diagram.

4) Expel the air from the test tube by gently turning on the <u>gas</u>. After about <u>5 seconds</u>, light the gas by holding a burning splint next to the hole in the end of the test tube. You can control the size of the flame by changing the <u>amount of gas</u> that's flowing through the test tube.

5) Use a Bunsen burner to heat the copper(II) oxide for about <u>10 minutes</u> (or until the solid changes colour from <u>black</u> to a <u>brownish-pink colour</u>).

6) Turn off the Bunsen burner and leave the test tube to <u>cool</u>.

7) Once the tube has cooled, <u>turn off</u> the gas and <u>weigh</u> the test tube with the bung and its contents.

burning gas · clamp · copper(II) oxide · gas · Bunsen burner

Once you've finished the experiment, you should have all the <u>data</u> you need to work out the <u>empirical formula</u> of the <u>copper(II) oxide</u> using the method on the previous page. Good stuff.

A red hot crucible — the scene of hotly contested snooker matches...

These two practicals are actually quite similar. In both of them you have to weigh the container three times — before you add the solid, after you add the solid and after the container has been heated. Convenient eh?

Q1   Describe how combustion could be used to determine the empirical formula of a metal oxide.   [4 marks]

Water of Crystallisation

Here's another page on <u>calculations</u> involving <u>experiments</u>. Don't worry, it's the last one for a while...

Salts Can be Anhydrous or Hydrated

1) All solid salts consist of a <u>lattice</u> of positive and negative <u>ions</u> (see page 17).

2) In some salts, <u>water molecules</u> are incorporated in the lattice too.

3) The water in a lattice is called <u>water of crystallisation</u>.

4) A solid salt containing water of crystallisation is <u>hydrated</u>.

5) If a salt <u>doesn't</u> contain any water of crystallisation, it's called <u>anhydrous</u>.

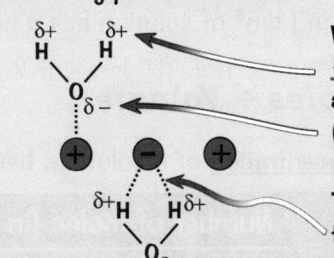

Here's a tiny part of the lattice in a <u>hydrated salt</u>:

Water molecules have a small <u>+ve charge</u> (δ^+) on the hydrogen atoms and a small <u>–ve charge</u> (δ^-) on the oxygen atoms.

This means they are <u>attracted</u> to the <u>ions</u> in the lattice and are <u>held in place</u>.

You Can Calculate How Much Water of Crystallisation a Salt Contains

1) One mole of a <u>hydrated salt</u> always has a <u>particular number of moles</u> of <u>water of crystallisation</u> — its <u>formula</u> shows <u>how many</u> (it's always a whole number).

2) For example, hydrated copper sulfate has <u>five moles of water</u> for every <u>one mole</u> of the salt. So its formula is $CuSO_4.5H_2O$. (Notice that there's a <u>dot</u> between the $CuSO_4$ and the $5H_2O$.)

3) Many hydrated salts <u>lose</u> their water of crystallisation when <u>heated</u>, to become <u>anhydrous</u>. If you know the mass of the salt when it's hydrated <u>and</u> when it's anhydrous, you can work its <u>formula</u> out like this:

Example: Heating hydrated magnesium sulfate, $MgSO_4.XH_2O$, in a crucible forms <u>anhydrous</u> magnesium sulfate, $MgSO_4$. Use the experimental data below to find the <u>value of X</u> and write the <u>formula</u> of the <u>hydrated salt</u>.

Mass of empty crucible	42.000 g
Mass of crucible + $MgSO_4.XH_2O$	45.210 g
Mass of crucible + $MgSO_4$	43.567 g

Method:

1) First, work out what <u>mass</u> of $MgSO_4.XH_2O$ and $MgSO_4$ you have.
   Mass of $MgSO_4.XH_2O$ = 45.210 − 42.000 = 3.210 g
   Mass of $MgSO_4$ = 43.567 − 42.000 = 1.567 g

2) Calculate the <u>number of moles</u> of <u>water lost</u>.
   Mass of water lost: 3.210 − 1.567 = 1.643 g
   Number of moles of water lost: mass $\div M_r$ = 1.643 g $\div$ 18 = 0.0913 moles

   $M_r\ H_2O = (2 \times 1) + 16 = 18$

3) Calculate the <u>number of moles</u> of <u>anhydrous salt</u> made.
   Molar mass of $MgSO_4$: 24 + 32 + (4 × 16) = 120 g
   Number of moles $MgSO_4$: mass $\div M_r$ = 1.567 $\div$ 120 = 0.0131 moles

4) Work out the <u>ratio of moles</u> of <u>anhydrous salt</u> to <u>moles of water</u>.
   From the experiment, 0.0131 moles of salt : 0.0913 moles of water,
   So, 1 mole of salt : (0.0913 $\div$ 0.0131) = 6.97 moles of water

5) <u>X</u> must be a <u>whole number</u>, and some errors are to be expected in any experiment, so you can <u>round off</u> your result — X = 7 and the formula of the hydrated salt is $MgSO_4.7H_2O$.

Anne Hydrous — the second wife of Henry VIII...

This working-out-the-formula business can be a bit tricky to get your head around at first — but if you follow exactly the same method each time you'll soon work it out. Oh, and don't forget the dot . it's very important.

Q1   Describe what is meant by the term 'water of crystallisation'.   [1 mark]

Moles and Concentration

Concentration is all about "<u>how much</u>" stuff you have in a <u>solution</u>.

Concentration is the 'Amount of Stuff' per Unit Volume

$1 \text{ dm}^3 = 1000 \text{ cm}^3 = 1 \text{ litre}$

1) The <u>concentration</u> of a solution is usually measured in <u>moles per dm³</u> (i.e. <u>moles per litre</u>). So 1 mole of stuff in 1 dm³ of solution has a concentration of <u>1 mole per dm³</u> (or 1 mol/dm³).

2) You might also sometimes see concentration being measured in <u>grams per dm³</u>. So 56 grams of stuff dissolved in 1 dm³ of solution has a concentration of <u>56 g per dm³</u> (or 56 g/dm³).

Concentration = No. of Moles ÷ Volume

1) If you ever have to find the <u>concentration</u> of a solution, here's the <u>formula</u> you'll need:

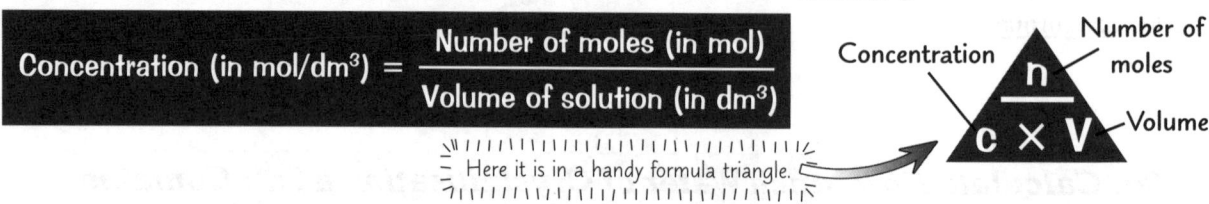

$$\text{Concentration (in mol/dm}^3) = \frac{\text{Number of moles (in mol)}}{\text{Volume of solution (in dm}^3)}$$

Here it is in a handy formula triangle.

Concentration — Number of moles / Volume

$$\frac{n}{c \times V}$$

> **Example:** What's the concentration of a solution with 2 moles of potassium iodide in 500 cm³?
>
> **Answer:** Easy — you've got 2 moles of potassium iodide and 500 cm³ = 0.5 dm³. So just stick these numbers in the formula: Concentration = 2 ÷ 0.5 = <u>4 mol/dm³</u>

2) You can use the same formula triangle to find the <u>number of moles</u> that are in a solution:

> **Example:** How many moles of sodium chloride are in 250 cm³ of a 3 mol/dm³ solution?
>
> **Answer:** 250 cm³ = 0.25 dm³. So, using the formula from the triangle...
> Number of moles = concentration × volume = 3 × 0.25 = <u>0.75 moles</u>

Converting Moles per dm³ to Grams per dm³

1) Calculating concentrations in <u>grams per dm³</u> is easy. You just divide the <u>mass</u> of the chemical in <u>grams</u> by the <u>volume</u> of solvent you used to dissolve it in <u>dm³</u>.

> **Example:** Give the concentration in g/dm³ of a solution made by dissolving 3 g of NaCl in 100 cm³ of water.
>
> **Answer:** Concentration = mass (g) ÷ volume (dm³) = 3 ÷ 0.1 = <u>30 g/dm³</u>

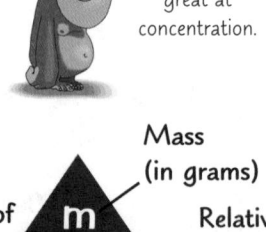

Murray wasn't great at concentration.

2) Changing a concentration from <u>mol/dm³</u> to <u>g/dm³</u> isn't too tricky. All you need to do is use the formula you met on page 25 to convert the <u>moles</u> per dm³ into <u>mass</u> per dm³.

Number of moles — Mass (in grams) — Relative formula mass

$$\frac{m}{n \times M_r}$$

> **Example:** You have a 0.04 mol/dm³ solution of sulfuric acid. What is the concentration in grams per dm³?
>
> **Step 1:** Work out the <u>relative formula mass</u> of the chemical.
> So, $H_2SO_4 = (1 \times 2) + 32 + (16 \times 4) = 98$
>
> **Step 2:** Convert the concentration in <u>moles</u> into concentration in <u>grams</u>.
> So, in 1 dm³: Mass in grams = moles × relative formula mass = 0.04 × 98 = 3.92 g
> So the concentration in g/dm³ = <u>3.92 g/dm³</u>

Learning this may take some concentration...

The main thing to learn on this page is the formula triangle for calculating concentration — remember that and concentration calculations should be a breeze. It'll come in handy when you do titrations too (see page 48).

Q1   How many moles of sodium hydroxide ($M_r = 40$) are in 200 cm³ of a 0.55 mol/dm³ solution?   [2 marks]

Calculating Volume

Run for your lives now, while you've still got the chance — it's <u>another formula</u>.

Avogadro's Law — One Mole of Any Gas Occupies 24 dm³

The space that <u>one mole</u> of a gas takes up is called its <u>molar volume</u>.
Here's a handy fact about molar volume that you definitely <u>need to learn</u>:

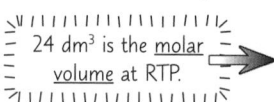
24 dm³ is the <u>molar volume</u> at RTP.

> One mole of <u>any gas</u> always occupies <u>24 dm³</u> (= 24 000 cm³) at room temperature and pressure (RTP: 20 °C and 1 atmosphere)

This means you can use the formula below to convert the number of moles of <u>any</u> gas at RTP to a <u>volume</u>:

$$\text{Volume (dm}^3\text{)} = \text{moles of gas} \times 24$$

If you need to work out the moles of gas from its mass, use the formula moles = mass ÷ M_r (see page 25).

Example 1: What's the volume of 4.5 moles of chlorine at RTP?

Answer: volume of 1 mole = 24 dm³, so volume of 4.5 moles = 4.5 × 24 dm³ = <u>108 dm³</u>

Example 2: How many moles are there in 8280 cm³ of hydrogen gas at RTP?

Answer: Number of moles = $\dfrac{\text{Volume of gas}}{\text{Volume of 1 mole}}$ = $\dfrac{8.28}{24}$ = <u>0.345 moles</u>

Don't forget to convert from cm³ to dm³.

You Can Calculate Volumes in Reactions If You Know the Masses

For this type of question there are <u>three stages</u>:

1) Calculate the <u>moles</u> of the <u>substance</u> you know the <u>mass</u> of.
2) <u>Find the moles of gas</u> using the balanced equation.
3) Then <u>convert the moles into a volume</u> using the formula above.

Example: Find the volume of carbon dioxide produced at RTP when 2.4 g of carbon is completely burned in oxygen. (A_r of carbon = 12, A_r of oxygen = 16)

1) Write out the <u>balanced equation</u>: $C + O_2 \rightarrow CO_2$

2) Work out the <u>relative formula mass</u> of the substance you know the mass of: M_r of C = 12

3) <u>Calculate the number of moles</u> of carbon in 2.4 g:
   moles = mass ÷ M_r = 2.4 ÷ 12 = 0.2

4) Look at the <u>ratio</u> of moles in the equation — 1 mole of C reacts to produce 1 mole of CO_2.
   So <u>0.2 moles</u> of <u>C</u> will react to produce <u>0.2 moles</u> of <u>CO_2</u>.

5) Use the formula above to work out the <u>volume</u>:
   volume = moles × 24 = 0.2 × 24 = <u>4.8 dm³</u>

Guacamole Law Firm

Avocado's Law — how many moles in a pot of guacamole...

Don't let molar volumes ruin your life — make sure you can use and rearrange the formula, and all will be fine.

Q1 The M_r of methane (CH_4) is 16. What volume will 36 g of methane gas occupy at RTP? [2 marks]

Q2 How much gas is produced when 11.5 g of sodium (Na, A_r = 23) is reacted with excess water at RTP?
The symbol equation for the reaction is: $2Na_{(s)} + 2H_2O_{(l)} \rightarrow 2NaOH_{(aq)} + H_{2(g)}$ [3 marks]

Paper 2

P2

Electrolysis

And now for something completely different... We're about to embark on some electrolysis. What a treat.

Electrolysis Involves Oxidation and Reduction

1) Electrolysis is the breaking down of a substance using electricity. An electric current is passed through an electrolyte (a molten or dissolved ionic compound), causing it to decompose.

See page 37 for more on oxidation and reduction.

2) In electrolysis, oxidation (loss of electrons) and reduction (gain of electrons) occur.

3) The positive ions (cations) in the electrolyte move towards the cathode (negative electrode) and are reduced (gain electrons).

4) The negative ions (anions) in the electrolyte move towards the anode (positive electrode) and are oxidised (lose electrons).

This creates a flow of charge through the electrolyte.

5) As ions gain or lose electrons they form the uncharged substances and are discharged from the electrolyte.

Ionic half equations show how electrons are transferred during reactions. They're really useful for showing what happens at each electrode during electrolysis. To write a half equation:

1) Put one of the things being oxidised or reduced on one side of an arrow, and the thing it gets oxidised or reduced to on the other.

2) Balance up the numbers of atoms just like in a normal equation.

3) Then add electrons (written e^-) on to one side to balance up the charges.

The charges on each side of the equation should balance.

Examples: Sodium is losing one electron to become a sodium ion: $Na \rightarrow Na^+ + e^-$
Hydrogen ions are gaining electrons to become hydrogen: $2H^+ + 2e^- \rightarrow H_2$

In Molten Ionic Compounds, There's Only One Source of Ions

1) Molten ionic compounds can be electrolysed because the ions can move freely.

2) They're usually broken up into their elements.

3) A good example of this is the electrolysis of molten lead bromide ($PbBr_2$).

4) You can write half-equations to show what's happening at each electrode.

You can melt lead bromide using a Bunsen burner.

5) The +ve Pb^{2+} ions are attracted to the –ve cathode. At the cathode a lead ion accepts two electrons and is reduced to a lead atom: $Pb^{2+} + 2e^- \rightarrow Pb$

6) The –ve Br^- ions are attracted to the +ve anode. At the anode two bromide ions lose one electron each and are oxidised to a bromine molecule: $2Br^- \rightarrow Br_2 + 2e^-$

flow of electrons — flow of electrons — anode (+ve) — cathode (–ve) — Lead is produced at the cathode. — Molten lead bromide — Bromine is produced at the anode. — Molten lead metal sinks to the bottom

7) The electrodes are made from an inert (unreactive) material so they don't take part in the reaction.

8) It's easy to predict what products you get when you electrolyse molten substances — but you need to get the half equations right too. Here are some examples:

Molten Electrolyte	Product at Cathode	Half equation at Cathode	Product at Anode	Half equation at Anode
potassium chloride, KCl	potassium	$K^+ + e^- \rightarrow K$	chlorine	$2Cl^- \rightarrow Cl_2 + 2e^-$
aluminium oxide, Al_2O_3	aluminium	$Al^{3+} + 3e^- \rightarrow Al$	oxygen	$2O^{2-} \rightarrow O_2 + 4e^-$

I told a chemistry joke at a party — it went down like a lead balloon...

Fed up with electrolysis? Probably best to take a short break before you turn over the page...

Q1 At which electrode does oxidation happen during electrolysis? [1 mark]

Section 3 — Equations, Calculations and Electrolysis

Electrolysis of Aqueous Solutions — PRACTICAL

Here's another lovely page all about <u>electrolysis</u>. Enjoy.

Here's How to Set Up an Electrochemical Cell

1) An <u>electrochemical cell</u> is a <u>circuit</u>, made up of the anode, cathode, electrolyte, a power source and the wires that connect the two electrodes.

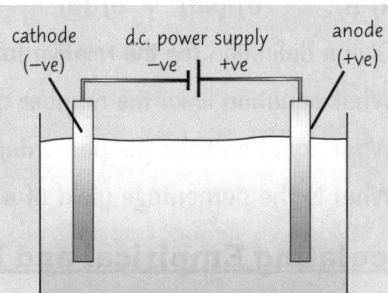
You could put an ammeter or bulb in series with your circuit to check you've set it up correctly.

2) You need to know how to <u>set up</u> an electrochemical cell for an <u>aqueous solution</u>. Here's how you'd do it:

1) Get <u>two inert electrodes</u>, e.g. graphite or platinum electrodes.
2) Clean the surfaces of the electrodes using some <u>emery paper</u> (or sandpaper).
3) From this point on, be careful <u>not to touch</u> the surfaces of the electrodes with your hands — you could transfer grease back onto the strips.
4) Place both electrodes into a <u>beaker</u> filled with your <u>electrolyte</u>.
5) Connect the electrodes to a power supply using <u>crocodile clips</u> and <u>wires</u>. When you turn the power supply on, a <u>current</u> will flow through the cell.

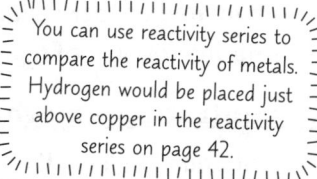

Electrolysis of Aqueous Solutions Involves the Ions From Water

1) In <u>aqueous solutions</u>, as well as the <u>ions</u> from the ionic compound, there will be <u>hydrogen ions</u> (H^+) and <u>hydroxide ions</u> (OH^-) from the <u>water</u>.

2) At the <u>cathode</u>, if <u>H^+ ions and metal ions</u> are present, <u>hydrogen gas</u> will be produced if the metal is <u>more reactive</u> than hydrogen (e.g. sodium). If the metal is <u>less reactive</u> than hydrogen (e.g. copper or silver), then a solid layer of the <u>pure metal</u> will be produced instead.

You can use reactivity series to compare the reactivity of metals. Hydrogen would be placed just above copper in the reactivity series on page 42.

3) At the <u>anode</u>, if <u>OH^- and halide ions</u> (Cl^-, Br^-, I^-) are present, molecules of chlorine, bromine or iodine will be formed. If <u>no halide ions</u> are present, then <u>oxygen</u> will be formed.

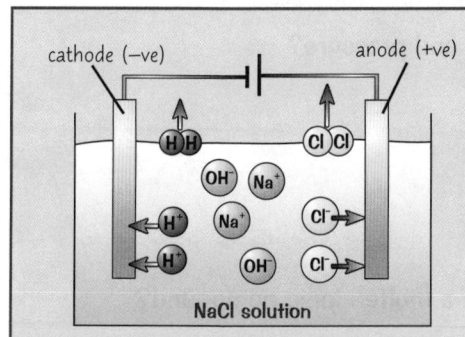

NaCl solution

A solution of <u>sodium chloride</u> (NaCl) contains <u>four different ions</u>: Na^+, Cl^-, OH^- and H^+.

- <u>Sodium</u> metal is more reactive hydrogen. So at the cathode, <u>hydrogen gas</u> is produced.
$$2H^+ + 2e^- \rightarrow H_2$$

- <u>Chloride ions</u> are present in the solution. So at the anode, <u>chlorine gas</u> is produced.
$$2Cl^- \rightarrow Cl_2 + 2e^-$$

Sir Chlo Ride

Sir Chlo Rode

4) You need to be able to <u>predict</u> the <u>products</u> when an aqueous solution is <u>electrolysed</u>. Here are some examples:

Aqueous Electrolyte	Product at Cathode	Half equation at Cathode	Product at Anode	Half equation at Anode
copper(II) sulfate, $CuSO_4$	copper	$Cu^{2+} + 2e^- \rightarrow Cu$	oxygen	$4OH^- \rightarrow O_2 + 2H_2O + 4e^-$
dilute sulfuric acid, H_2O/H_2SO_4	hydrogen	$2H^+ + 2e^- \rightarrow H_2$	oxygen	$4OH^- \rightarrow O_2 + 2H_2O + 4e^-$

You might see the half equation for this reaction at the anode written like this: $2H_2O \rightarrow 4H^+ + O_2 + 4e^-$

Two electrodes and a lake of fire — electrochemical hell...

So it's kinda confusing this electrolysis malarkey — you need to take it slow and make sure you get it.

Q1   Describe how an electrochemical cell could be set up to electrolyse an aqueous solution. [3 marks]

Q2   An aqueous solution of copper bromide, $CuBr_2$, is electrolysed using inert electrodes. Give the half equation to show the reaction occurring at the anode. [2 marks]

Paper 2

Revision Questions for Section 3

That's the end of <u>Section 3</u>. Give yourself a pat on the back — and then...

- ...try these questions and <u>tick off each one</u> when you <u>get it right</u>.
- When you've done <u>all the questions</u> under a heading and are <u>completely happy</u> with it, tick it off.

Calculating Masses and Moles (p.23-26) ☐

1) What do the following state symbols stand for?
   a) (l)   b) (aq)   c) (g)
2) Give a definition for the relative formula mass of a compound.
3) What equation links the number of moles with the mass and M_r of a substance?
4) What equation links the percentage yield with the actual and theoretical yields?
5) What is the percentage yield of a reaction where no products are made?

Calculating Empirical and Molecular Formulae (p.27-29) ☐

6) What is the empirical formula of a compound?
7) How does the molecular formula of a compound relate to its empirical formula?
8) Outline an experiment involving reduction that you could
   use to work out the empirical formula of copper oxide.
9) In hydrated copper sulfate, for every one mole of salt, there are five moles of water.
   Write the formula of hydrated copper sulfate ($CuSO_4$).

Concentration and Volume (p.30-31) ☐

10) What equation links the concentration of a solution with its volume and the number of moles present?
11) Describe how to convert a concentration from moles/dm³ to g/dm³.
12) What is the 'molar volume' of a gas?
13) What volume does one mole of gas occupy at room temperature and pressure?

Electrolysis (p.32-33) ☐

14) What is electrolysis?
15) What is a cation?
16) Towards which electrode do the anions in an electrolyte move?
17) At which electrode does the metal form during the electrolysis of a molten ionic compound?
18) Name the components of an electrochemical cell.
19) Write a half equation to show what happens at the cathode
    in the electrolysis of sodium chloride solution, NaCl.
20) Name the products formed when a solution of copper sulfate is electrolysed.

Group 1 — The Alkali Metals

Group 1 elements are known as the <u>alkali metals</u>. As metals go, they're pretty <u>reactive</u>.

Group 1 Elements All React in a Similar Way with Water

1) <u>Simple reactions</u> can be used to work out if an element is part of the same <u>family</u> as other elements. Elements of the same family will react in a similar way.

2) For example, when <u>lithium</u>, <u>sodium</u> and <u>potassium</u> are put in <u>water</u>, they all react <u>vigorously</u>.

3) The <u>reaction</u> produces a <u>metal hydroxide</u> solution. This solution is <u>alkaline</u> — this is why Group 1 elements are known as the <u>alkali metals</u>.

4) The <u>reaction</u> of the alkali metals with water also produces <u>hydrogen</u> — this is why you can see <u>fizzing</u>.

5) These reactions can be written as <u>chemical equations</u> — e.g. for <u>sodium</u> the equation is...

Word equation:	sodium + water → sodium hydroxide + hydrogen
Symbol equation:	$2Na_{(s)} + 2H_2O_{(l)} \rightarrow 2NaOH_{(aq)} + H_{2(g)}$

STATE SYMBOLS:
(s) = <u>solid</u>, (l) = <u>liquid</u>, (g) = <u>gas</u>,
(aq) = <u>aqueous</u> (dissolved in water)

6) The Group 1 metals can also react with <u>oxygen</u> in the air to form <u>metal oxides</u>. ◄ This is why they tarnish when left in air, leaving a dull metal oxide layer.

7) Different <u>types of oxide</u> will form depending on the Group 1 metal:

- Lithium reacts to form <u>lithium oxide</u> (Li_2O).
- Sodium reacts to form a mixture of <u>sodium oxide</u> (Na_2O) and <u>sodium peroxide</u> (Na_2O_2).
- Potassium reacts to form a mixture of <u>potassium peroxide</u> (K_2O_2) and <u>potassium superoxide</u> (KO_2).

Group 1 Elements Become More Reactive Down the Group

1) As you go <u>down</u> Group 1 the elements become <u>more reactive</u>.

2) You can see this in the <u>rate of reaction</u> with water (i.e. the time taken for a lump of the same size of each element to <u>react completely</u> with the water and disappear).

3) <u>Lithium</u> takes longer than sodium or potassium to react, so it's the <u>least reactive</u>.

4) <u>Potassium</u> takes the shortest time to react of these three elements, so it's the <u>most reactive</u>.

5) The <u>trend in reactivity</u> can also be seen in the reaction between the alkali metals and <u>oxygen</u>. Potassium reacts to form its oxide <u>quicker</u> than sodium and lithium when left in <u>air</u>.

6) You can use the trend in reactivity to <u>predict</u> how other group 1 metals will react.

The elements in Group 1 get more reactive as the atomic number increases.

Group 1	Group 2
7 Li Lithium 3	Be
23 Na Sodium 11	Mg
39 K Potassium 19	Ca
86 Rb Rubidium 37	Sr
133 Cs Caesium 55	Ba
223 Fr Francium 87	Ra

Friends, alkali metals, countrymen... Tell me your trends.

E.g. you could predict that <u>caesium</u> will react <u>more vigorously</u> than potassium with <u>water</u> (in fact, it <u>explodes</u>).

Atoms Lose Electrons More Easily Down the Group

1) All <u>Group 1</u> metals have <u>1 electron</u> in their outer shell.

2) As you go <u>down</u> Group 1, the <u>outermost electron</u> is in a shell that's <u>further from the nucleus</u>.

3) Which means the <u>attraction</u> between the <u>outermost electron</u> and the <u>nucleus</u> becomes <u>less</u>.

4) So as you go down Group 1 the atoms get <u>bigger</u>, the outer electron is <u>more easily lost</u>, and the metals are <u>more reactive</u>.

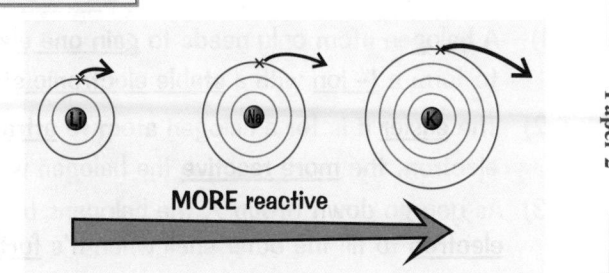

MORE reactive

My cat is from group 1 — it reacts vigorously with water...

Alkali metals are ace. They're so reactive you have to store them in oil — because otherwise they'd react with the air.

Q1   Write a balanced symbol equation for the reaction between potassium (K) and water.   [2 marks]

Group 7 — The Halogens

Here's a page on another periodic table group that you need to be familiar with — the halogens.

HALOGEN — Seven Letters — Group 7

1) The elements in Group 7 of the periodic table are called the halogens.

2) As the atomic number of the halogens increases, the elements have a darker colour and a higher boiling point. This means at room temperature:

- **Chlorine** (Cl_2) is a fairly reactive, poisonous, green gas.

- **Bromine** (Br_2) is a poisonous, red-brown liquid, which gives off an orange vapour at room temperature.

- **Iodine** (I_2) is a dark grey crystalline solid which gives off a purple vapour when heated.

	Group 6	Group 7	Group 0
			He
	O	19 F Fluorine 9	Ne
	S	35.5 Cl Chlorine 17	Ar
	Se	80 Br Bromine 35	Kr
	Te	127 I Iodine 53	Xe
	Po	210 At Astatine 85	Rn

3) This table shows how the properties of the elements in Group 7 gradually change as you go down the group:

Group VII Elements	Properties			
	Atomic number	Colour	Physical state at room temperature	Boiling point
Chlorine	17	green	gas	−34 °C
Bromine	35	red-brown	liquid	59 °C
Iodine	53	dark grey	solid	185 °C

4) The higher up Group 7 an element is, the more reactive it is.

5) You might need to use these trends to predict the properties of other halogens.

> **E.g.** You can see that boiling point increases down the group, and the colours of the halogens get darker, so you could predict that astatine (which comes below iodine) would be a dark-coloured solid at room temperature. Sure enough, astatine is a black solid with a melting point of around 300 °C.

Reactivity Decreases Going Down Group 7

1) A halogen atom only needs to gain one electron to form a 1– ion with a stable electronic structure.

2) The easier it is for a halogen atom to attract an electron, the more reactive the halogen will be.

3) As you go down Group 7, the halogens become less reactive — it gets harder to attract the extra electron to fill the outer shell when it's further away from the nucleus (the atomic radius is larger).

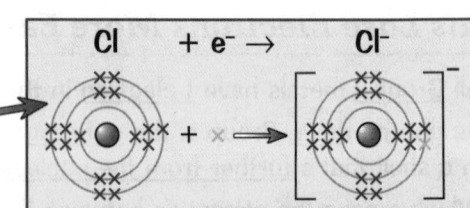

Halogens — one electron short of a full shell...

Another page, another periodic table group to learn the properties and the trends of. It's like Christmas come early.

Q1   How do the boiling points of the halogens change as you go down the group?   [1 mark]

Section 4 — Inorganic Chemistry

Displacement Reactions

The <u>halogens</u> are a pretty competitive lot really. In fact the <u>more reactive ones</u> will push the <u>less reactive ones</u> out of a compound. How uncivilized — has nobody ever taught them that it's bad manners to push?

More Reactive Halogens will Displace Less Reactive Ones

1) The elements in Group 7 take part in <u>displacement reactions</u>.

2) A <u>displacement reaction</u> is where a <u>more reactive</u> element "<u>pushes out</u>" (displaces) a <u>less reactive</u> element from a compound.

3) For example, <u>chlorine</u> is more reactive than <u>iodine</u> (it's higher up Group 7).

4) So, if you add <u>chlorine water</u> to <u>potassium iodide</u> solution the chlorine will react with the potassium in the potassium iodide to form <u>potassium chloride</u>.

5) The <u>iodine</u> is <u>displaced from the salt</u> and gets left in the solution, turning it <u>brown</u>.

6) The table below shows what happens when you mix different combinations of <u>chlorine</u>, <u>bromine</u> and <u>iodine</u> with the salts <u>potassium chloride</u>, <u>potassium bromide</u> and <u>potassium iodide</u>.

chlorine water

colourless solution — potassium iodide

brown solution — iodine forming in solution

Start with:	Potassium chloride solution $KCl_{(aq)}$ — colourless	Potassium bromide solution $KBr_{(aq)}$ — colourless	Potassium iodide solution $KI_{(aq)}$ — colourless
Add chlorine water $Cl_{2\,(aq)}$ — colourless	no reaction	orange solution (Br_2) formed	brown solution (I_2) formed
Add bromine water $Br_{2\,(aq)}$ — orange	no reaction	no reaction	brown solution (I_2) formed
Add iodine water $I_{2\,(aq)}$ — brown	no reaction	no reaction	no reaction

These experiments are dead easy. All you need to do is add a few drops of the halogen solution to the salt solution. Then look for a colour change.

Halogen Displacement Reactions Involve Transfer of Electrons

1) You can show the <u>displacement reactions</u> between halogens and salt solutions as <u>equations</u>. E.g.

$$Cl_2(aq) + 2KI(aq) \rightarrow I_2(aq) + 2KCl(aq)$$

This is the equation for chlorine displacing iodine from potassium iodide. They might give you a different example in the exam, but the principle is always the same.

2) When this reaction happens <u>electrons</u> are <u>passed</u> from the iodine to the chlorine.

Each chlorine atom in the Cl_2 molecule gains an electron to form two negative Cl^- ions.

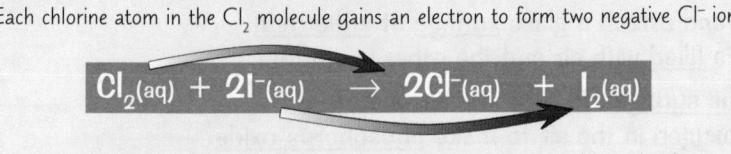

$$Cl_2(aq) + 2I^-_{(aq)} \rightarrow 2Cl^-_{(aq)} + I_2(aq)$$

Two iodide ions lose an electron each and then form a neutral I_2 molecule.

3) A <u>loss of electrons</u> is called <u>oxidation</u>. A <u>gain in electrons</u> is called <u>reduction</u>. Oxidation and reduction can also describe the gain and loss of oxygen — see p.44.

4) In displacement reactions, reduction and oxidation happen <u>simultaneously</u>. For example, in this reaction the <u>chlorine is reduced</u> and the <u>iodine is oxidised</u>.

You can remember which is which by using OIL RIG. Oxidation Is Loss, Reduction Is Gain (of electrons).

5) An <u>oxidising agent</u> accepts electrons and <u>gets reduced</u>. So, here <u>chlorine</u> is an oxidising agent.

6) A <u>reducing agent</u> donates electrons and <u>gets oxidised</u>. So <u>iodine</u> is a reducing agent.

7) Reactions where reduction and oxidation happen at the same time are called <u>redox reactions</u>.

New information displaces old information from my brain...

If you remember that the halogens get less reactive as you go down the group, you can work out what will happen when you mix any halogen with any halide salt. You need to know the colour changes that go with the reactions too.

Q1 A student added a few drops of a halogen solution to a potassium iodide solution. The solution turned brown. Explain what the student should do to help him identify the halogen solution. [2 marks]

Gases in the Atmosphere

This page is all about the gases in our <u>atmosphere</u> — what a breath of fresh air...

The Atmosphere is Mostly Nitrogen and Oxygen

For <u>200 million years</u> or so, the atmosphere has been about how it is now:

- **78%** <u>nitrogen</u>
- nearly **1%** <u>argon</u>
- **21%** <u>oxygen</u>
- only **0.04%** <u>carbon dioxide</u>

There can be a lot of water vapour too.

Make sure you know the <u>proportions</u> of each <u>gas</u>.

You can Investigate the Proportion of Oxygen in the Atmosphere   PRACTICAL

1) <u>Iron</u> can be used to determine the percentage of oxygen in the air.

2) This is because <u>iron</u> reacts with oxygen in the air to form <u>rust</u>
(see page 43) — so iron will <u>remove oxygen</u> from the air.

Here's how you'd do this experiment:

- First soak some <u>iron wool</u> in <u>acetic acid</u> (the acid will catalyse the reaction). Then push the wool into a <u>measuring cylinder</u> and invert the measuring cylinder into a beaker of water.
- Record the <u>starting position</u> of the water using the scale on the measuring cylinder — this is the starting volume of air.
- Over time, the level of the water in the measuring cylinder will <u>rise</u>.
- This is because the iron <u>reacts</u> with the <u>oxygen</u> in the air to make iron oxide. The water rises to fill the space the oxygen took up.
- Leave the measuring cylinder for <u>around a week</u> or until the water level <u>stops changing</u>.
- Record the <u>finishing</u> position of the water — this is the final volume of air.

Iron wool

Finishing position of water.

Starting position of water.

Water

To calculate the percentage of oxygen just put the volumes you recorded into this <u>formula</u>: The answer you get should be about <u>20%</u>.

$$\frac{\text{Start volume} - \text{Final volume}}{\text{Start volume}} \times 100$$

3) You can also use <u>phosphorus</u> to determine the percentage of oxygen in the air. Here's how:

- Place the <u>phosphorus</u> in a tube and attach a glass <u>syringe</u> at <u>either end</u>. Make sure one of the syringes is <u>filled</u> with air and the other is <u>empty</u>.
- <u>Heat</u> the phosphorus and use the syringes to pass the air over it — the phosphorus will react with oxygen in the air to make <u>phosphorus oxide</u>.

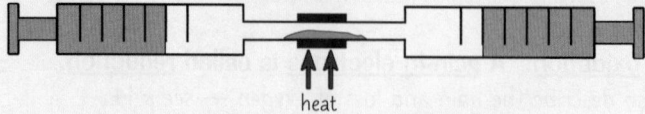

heat

Push all the air into one syringe to measure the final volume.

- As it reacts, the amount of air in the syringes will <u>decrease</u>.
- Measure the <u>starting</u> and <u>final volumes</u> of air using the <u>scale</u> on one of the syringes.
- You can then calculate the <u>percentage</u> of oxygen in the air using the <u>formula above</u>.

I went to a restaurant on the moon — nice view, no atmosphere...

So most of the gas we breath in is nitrogen, seems like a waste of breath if you ask me. What isn't a waste of breath is using iron or phosphorus to work out how much oxygen is in the air. Make sure you learn the nifty methods and how to calculate your answer to the percentage too. Then, use some oxygen to make yourself some tea.

Q1   What are the four most abundant gases in dry air?   [1 mark]

Q2   Explain how phosphorus and iron can be used to calculate the percentage of oxygen in air.   [2 marks]

Gases in Reactions

Lots of reactions involve <u>gases</u>, sometimes as <u>reactants</u>, sometimes as <u>products</u>. Here's a whole page on them...

When you Burn Something it Reacts with Oxygen in Air

When an element is burnt in air it <u>reacts</u> with the oxygen to form an <u>oxide</u>.
These oxides can have either <u>acidic</u> or <u>basic</u> character (see page 46).
Here are some examples you need to <u>know</u>:

Magnesium

<u>Magnesium</u> burns with a <u>bright white flame</u> in air and
the <u>white powder</u> that is formed is <u>magnesium oxide</u>.
Magnesium oxide is slightly <u>alkaline</u> when it's dissolved in water.

$$2Mg_{(s)} + O_{2(g)} \rightarrow 2MgO_{(s)}$$

Hydrogen

<u>Hydrogen</u> burns <u>very easily</u> in oxygen, in fact it can be <u>explosive</u>.
It has an <u>orangey/yellow flame</u> and the only product is <u>water</u> (as water vapour).

$$2H_{2(g)} + O_{2(g)} \rightarrow 2H_2O_{(g)}$$

The combustion of hydrogen is often used as a <u>test</u> for hydrogen gas.
In small amounts, the resulting explosion gives the characteristic '<u>squeaky pop</u>' (see p.53).

Sulfur

<u>Sulfur</u> burns in air or oxygen with a <u>pale blue flame</u> and produces <u>sulfur dioxide</u>.
Sulfur dioxide is <u>acidic</u> when it's dissolved in water.

$$S_{(s)} + O_{2(g)} \rightarrow SO_{2(g)}$$

The Thermal Decomposition of Metal Carbonates Produces CO$_2$

1) If you <u>heat</u> a <u>metal carbonate</u>, you get <u>carbon dioxide</u> and a <u>metal oxide</u>.

2) This is an example of <u>thermal decomposition</u>, which is when a substance <u>breaks down</u> into simpler substances <u>when heated</u>.

3) <u>Copper(II) carbonate</u> is a <u>green powder</u> that will easily decompose to form <u>carbon dioxide</u> and <u>copper(II) oxide</u> when you heat it.

4) <u>Here's the equation</u> for the thermal decomposition of copper(II) carbonate:

$$CuCO_{3(s)} \rightarrow CuO_{(s)} + CO_{2(g)}$$

copper(II) carbonate → copper oxide + carbon dioxide

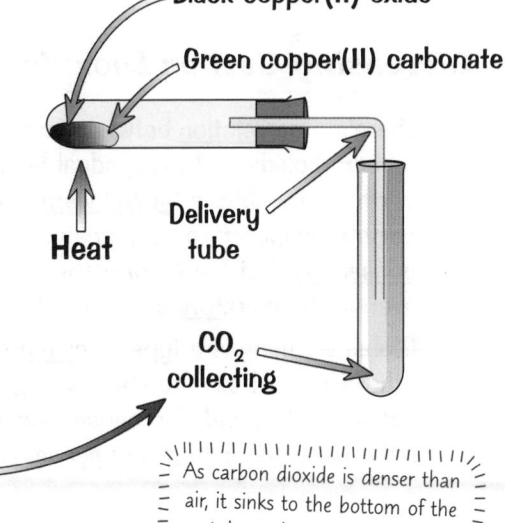

5) To do the experiment, heat <u>copper(II) carbonate</u> then collect the gas that's given off in a <u>test tube</u>.

6) The gas that is collected can then be <u>tested</u> to see if it is CO$_2$ using the method on page 53.

As carbon dioxide is denser than air, it sinks to the bottom of the tube and can be collected.

Revision getting tough? No need to sulfur in silence...

CO$_2$ can be pretty useful stuff. If you are wondering where, it's the stuff that makes cakes rise — and we all love cakes that rise. Make sure you learn how to describe the production of CO$_2$ through the thermal decomposition of carbonates.

Q1　What gas is produced when sulfur is burnt?　[1 mark]

Carbon Dioxide

You've probably heard of carbon dioxide, it's always in the news. This page will tell you why.

Carbon Dioxide is a Greenhouse Gas

1) The temperature of the Earth is a balance between the heat it gets from the Sun and the heat it radiates back out into space.

2) Gases in the atmosphere like carbon dioxide, methane and water vapour naturally act like an insulating layer. They are often called 'greenhouse gases'. They absorb most of the heat that would normally be radiated out into space, and re-radiate it in all directions — including back towards the Earth.

3) Human activity affects the amount of carbon dioxide in the atmosphere — examples include:

- Deforestation: fewer trees means less CO_2 is removed from the atmosphere via photosynthesis.
- Burning fossil fuels: carbon that was 'locked up' in these fuels is being released as CO_2.

4) It is because of this human activity that over the last 200 years or so, the concentration of carbon dioxide in the atmosphere has been increasing. For this to have happened, CO_2 must be being released into the air faster than it's being removed — this is linked to climate change (see below).

Increasing Carbon Dioxide is Linked to Climate Change

1) There's a correlation between increasing levels of carbon dioxide and the gradual heating up of the Earth's atmosphere (global warming). Although the Earth's temperature varies naturally, there's a scientific consensus that the extra carbon dioxide has caused the average temperature of the Earth to increase.

2) Global warming is a type of climate change and causes other types of climate change, e.g. changing rainfall patterns. It could also cause severe flooding due to the polar ice caps melting and sea level rise.

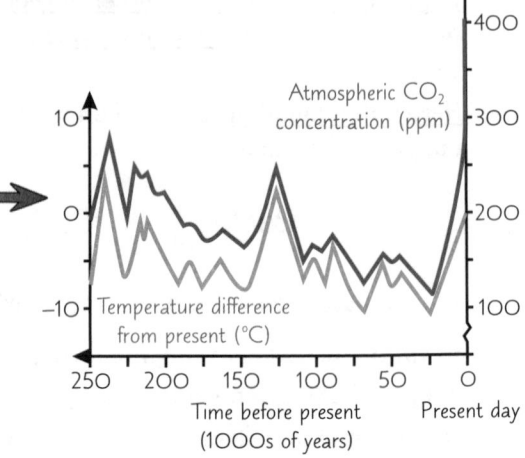

Give the climate some privacy — it's changing...

It's not all depressing news. There are steps we can take to cut our carbon dioxide emissions, so chin up.

Q1   Why is the concentration of CO_2 increasing?   [1 mark]

Q2   Explain how greenhouse gases affect the Earth's temperature.   [2 marks]

Reactions of Metals

Reactive metals tend to do exciting, fizzy things when you drop them into acid or water...

How Metals React With Acids Tells You About Their Reactivity

PRACTICAL

1) Some metals react with acids to produce a <u>salt</u> and <u>hydrogen gas</u>.

$$\text{Acid} + \text{Metal} \rightarrow \text{Salt} + \text{Hydrogen}$$

2) You can use the reactions of different metals with <u>dilute acids</u> to work out how <u>reactive</u> they are. The more <u>reactive</u> the metal, the <u>faster</u> the reaction will go — very reactive metals (e.g. sodium) react <u>explosively</u>.

3) You can carry out a practical to investigate the <u>differences in reactivity</u> of a variety of metals by using their reaction with acids.

4) First, set up <u>three boiling tubes</u> and fill them with <u>equal volumes</u> of <u>dilute hydrochloric acid</u> or <u>dilute sulfuric acid</u>.

The type of salt produced depends on the acid used — see page 47.

5) Then, place pieces of <u>magnesium</u>, <u>zinc</u> and <u>iron</u> in separate test tubes — make sure that the size and shape of the metal pieces is the same.

6) The <u>speed</u> of reaction is indicated by the <u>rate</u> at which the <u>bubbles</u> of hydrogen are given off.

7) The <u>hydrogen</u> is confirmed by the <u>burning splint test</u> (see page 53). The magnesium should give the loudest 'squeaky pop' as it has the most vigorous reaction producing the most hydrogen gas.

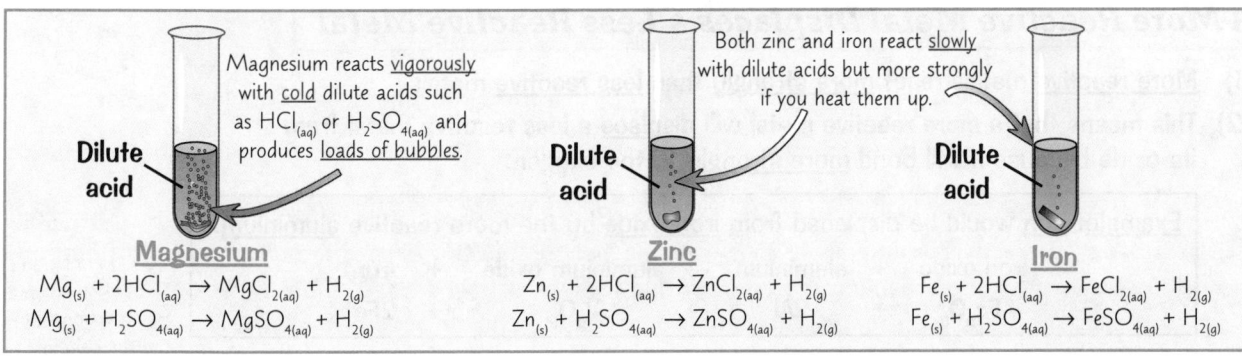

Magnesium reacts <u>vigorously</u> with <u>cold</u> dilute acids such as $HCl_{(aq)}$ or $H_2SO_{4(aq)}$ and produces <u>loads of bubbles</u>.

Both zinc and iron react <u>slowly</u> with dilute acids but more strongly if you heat them up.

Magnesium

$$Mg_{(s)} + 2HCl_{(aq)} \rightarrow MgCl_{2(aq)} + H_{2(g)}$$
$$Mg_{(s)} + H_2SO_{4(aq)} \rightarrow MgSO_{4(aq)} + H_{2(g)}$$

Zinc

$$Zn_{(s)} + 2HCl_{(aq)} \rightarrow ZnCl_{2(aq)} + H_{2(g)}$$
$$Zn_{(s)} + H_2SO_{4(aq)} \rightarrow ZnSO_{4(aq)} + H_{2(g)}$$

Iron

$$Fe_{(s)} + 2HCl_{(aq)} \rightarrow FeCl_{2(aq)} + H_{2(g)}$$
$$Fe_{(s)} + H_2SO_{4(aq)} \rightarrow FeSO_{4(aq)} + H_{2(g)}$$

Some Metals Also React With Water

The <u>reactions</u> of metals with <u>water</u> also show the reactivity of metals. This is the basic reaction:

$$\text{metal} + \text{water} \rightarrow \text{metal hydroxide} + \text{hydrogen}$$
(Or: less reactive metal + steam → metal oxide + hydrogen)

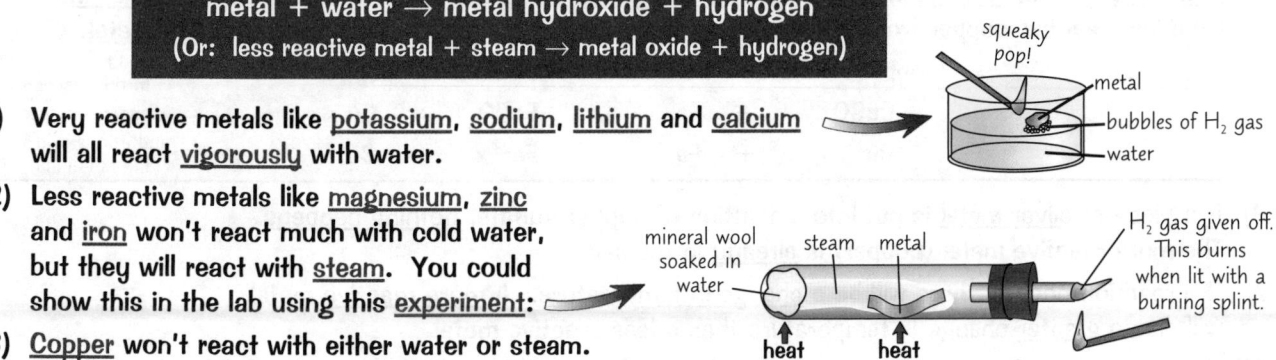

squeaky pop!
metal
bubbles of H_2 gas
water

1) Very reactive metals like <u>potassium</u>, <u>sodium</u>, <u>lithium</u> and <u>calcium</u> will all react <u>vigorously</u> with water.

2) Less reactive metals like <u>magnesium</u>, <u>zinc</u> and <u>iron</u> won't react much with cold water, but they will react with <u>steam</u>. You could show this in the lab using this <u>experiment</u>:

3) <u>Copper</u> won't react with either water or steam.

mineral wool soaked in water
steam metal
heat heat
H_2 gas given off. This burns when lit with a burning splint.

I AM NOT HIGHLY REACTIVE — OK...

See, experiments aren't just for fun — they can give you a thrilling insight into the relative reactivities of elements.

Q1 A student is given small samples of three metals, A, B and C. He places them in dilute hydrochloric acid. Nothing happens to Metal A. Metal B fizzes vigorously. The gas given off gives a loud squeaky pop when lit with a burning splint. Metal C fizzes a bit. The gas given off gives a quiet squeaky pop when lit.
Put the three metals in order, from most reactive to least reactive.

[1 mark]

The Reactivity Series

The previous page covered some reactions that help you work out how <u>reactive</u> a <u>metal</u> is. You can use this information to put the metals in order of their <u>reactivity</u>. Which is more useful than it sounds, promise.

The Reactivity Series — How Well a Metal Reacts

The <u>reactivity series</u> lists metals in <u>order</u> of their <u>reactivity</u> towards other substances.

Make sure you learn this list:

The Reactivity Series

Potassium	K	Very Reactive
Sodium	Na	
Lithium	Li	
Calcium	Ca	
Magnesium	Mg	Fairly Reactive
Aluminium	Al	
Zinc	Zn	
Iron	Fe	Not very Reactive
Copper	Cu	
Silver	Ag	
Gold	Au	Not at all Reactive

Catch....

Are you ready for some metal?

A More Reactive Metal Displaces a Less Reactive Metal

1) <u>More reactive</u> metals react <u>more strongly</u> than <u>less reactive</u> metals.

2) This means that a more reactive metal will <u>displace</u> a less reactive metal from its oxide because it will bond <u>more strongly</u> to the oxygen.

> <u>Example:</u> <u>iron</u> would be displaced from <u>iron oxide</u> by the more reactive <u>aluminium</u>.
>
> iron oxide   +   aluminium   →   aluminium oxide   +   iron
>
> Fe_2O_3 + $2Al$ → Al_2O_3 + $2Fe$

Oxidation and reduction can refer to the gain and loss of electrons (see p.37) or oxygen (see p.44).

3) Displacement reactions like the ones above are <u>redox reactions</u> (see p.37) — the metal is <u>oxidised</u> and the displaced metal ion is <u>reduced</u>.

4) <u>Metal compounds</u> like copper sulfate, zinc chloride and sodium chloride are <u>metal salts</u>.

5) If you put a <u>reactive metal</u> into a solution of a <u>less reactive metal salt</u> the reactive metal will <u>replace</u> the <u>less reactive metal</u> in the salt.

> <u>Example:</u> put an <u>iron nail</u> in a solution of <u>copper sulfate</u> and the more reactive iron will "<u>kick out</u>" the less reactive copper from the salt. You end up with <u>iron sulfate solution</u> and <u>copper metal</u>.
>
> copper sulfate   +   iron   →   iron sulfate   +   copper
>
> $CuSO_4$ + Fe → $FeSO_4$ + Cu
>
> Cu^{2+} + Fe → Fe^{2+} + Cu

In this reaction, copper is reduced and iron is oxidised.

6) If a piece of <u>silver metal</u> is put into a solution of copper sulfate, <u>nothing happens</u>. The more reactive metal (copper) is <u>already</u> in the salt.

7) If a reaction occurs, there will be a <u>change in temperature</u>. A <u>more reactive</u> metal will give a <u>greater</u> change in temperature than a less reactive metal.

8) You can use displacement reactions to <u>work out</u> where in the reactivity series a metal is supposed to go. For example, if you were given a lump of a mystery metal, you could try reacting it with different <u>metal oxides</u> and <u>salts</u>. If it <u>reacted</u> with copper oxide you'd know it was <u>higher</u> in the series than copper. If it <u>didn't react</u> with magnesium sulfate you'd know it was lower than magnesium in the reactivity series.

And that's why Iron Man never goes swimming in copper sulfate...

You could be given the results of an experiment and have to use them to put the metals into an order of reactivity, or you could be told their reactivities and then asked to predict how they'll react — make sure you can do both.

Q1   State whether silver would displace iron from iron chloride solution and explain your answer.   [1 mark]

Iron

Iron's <u>strength</u> has made it a very important metal that's used throughout the world for <u>building construction</u>, <u>car manufacture</u> and wrought iron <u>garden furniture</u>. But the problem is — it rusts...

Iron and Steel Corrode to Make Rust

1) Iron corrodes easily. In other words, it <u>rusts</u>.   The word "rust" is only used for the corrosion of iron, not other metals.
2) Rusting only happens when the iron's in contact with both <u>oxygen</u> (from the air) and <u>water</u>.
3) The chemical reaction that takes place when iron corrodes is an <u>oxidation</u> reaction — see next page. The iron <u>gains oxygen</u> to form <u>iron(III) oxide</u>.
4) Water then becomes loosely bonded to the iron(III) oxide and the result is <u>hydrated iron(III) oxide</u> — which we call rust.
5) Learn the <u>word equation</u> for the reaction:

> iron + oxygen + water → hydrated iron(III) oxide (rust)

6) Unfortunately, rust is a soft crumbly solid that soon <u>flakes off</u> to leave more iron available to <u>rust again</u>.

There are Two Main Ways to Prevent Rusting

1) The obvious way to prevent rusting is to <u>coat the iron</u> with a <u>barrier</u> to keep out the water and oxygen.

<u>BARRIER METHODS</u>:

<u>Painting</u>/<u>Coating with plastic</u> — ideal for big and small structures alike. It can be decorative too.

<u>Oiling</u>/<u>Greasing</u> — this has to be used when moving parts are involved, like on bike chains.

Jamie wanted to make sure his Nan didn't rust.

2) The other way is the <u>sacrificial method</u>. This involves placing a <u>more reactive metal</u> with the iron. The water and oxygen then react with this sacrificial metal <u>instead</u> of with the iron.

- <u>Zinc</u> is often used as a sacrificial metal.
- The zinc is <u>more reactive</u> than iron — it's further up the reactivity series.
- So, the zinc will be oxidised <u>instead</u> of the iron.
- A <u>coating of zinc</u> can be sprayed onto the object — this is known as <u>galvanising</u>.
- Or big <u>blocks of zinc</u> can be bolted to the iron. This is used on ships' hulls, or on underground iron pipes.

My old robot friend died yesterday — may he rust in peace...

Rust gets everywhere. On my car, my old bike, now in your exam. Best get some practice in now...

Q1   Outline how bolting some magnesium onto a piece of iron will prevent it from rusting.   [2 marks]

Q2   Name two substances required for iron to rust.   [2 marks]

Metals and Redox

Most metals can't be found as pure lumps. You have to <u>extract</u> them from a <u>compound</u>. This involves reduction.

Oxidation is the Addition of Oxygen, Reduction is the Removal of Oxygen

1) <u>Oxidation</u> can mean the <u>reaction with</u>, or <u>addition of oxygen</u>. <u>Reduction</u> can be the <u>removal of oxygen</u>.

<u>OXIDATION — GAIN OF OXYGEN</u>
Magnesium is <u>oxidised</u> to magnesium oxide.

$$2Mg + O_2 \rightarrow 2MgO$$

<u>REDUCTION — LOSS OF OXYGEN</u>
Copper oxide is <u>reduced</u> to copper using carbon.

$$2CuO + C \rightarrow 2Cu + CO_2$$

2) In an oxidation reaction, the substance that <u>oxidises</u> the metal (and is reduced) is the <u>oxidising</u> agent.
In a reduction reaction, the substance that <u>reduces</u> the metal (and is oxidised) is called the <u>reducing agent</u>.

Most Metals are Found in Ores and have to be Separated

1) Metals that are <u>unreactive</u> don't tend to form <u>compounds</u> with other elements. Unreactive metals such as <u>gold</u> are found <u>uncombined</u> — so you just have to find them and dig 'em up.

2) However, most metals <u>do react</u> with other elements to form compounds, which can be found naturally in the <u>Earth's crust</u>. If a compound contains enough of the metal to make it <u>worthwhile extracting</u>, the compound is called a <u>metal ore</u>. There are <u>limited amounts</u> of metal ores — they're "<u>finite resources</u>".

3) The <u>more reactive</u> a metal is, the <u>harder it is to extract it from a compound</u>.

4) Lots of common metals like <u>iron</u> and <u>aluminium</u> form <u>metal oxide</u> ores.
The metal can be <u>separated</u> from its oxide by a <u>reduction reaction</u>.

5) The most common type of reduction reaction uses <u>carbon</u> as a <u>reducing agent</u> to separate the oxygen from the metal.

$$2Fe_2O_3 + 3C \rightarrow 4Fe + 3CO_2$$
iron oxide + carbon → iron + carbon dioxide

6) But carbon can't be used for all metals...

Methods of Extraction are Linked to the Order of Reactivity

1) Only metals that are <u>less reactive</u> than <u>carbon</u> can be extracted by a reduction reaction with carbon — this is done by <u>heating</u> the ore with <u>carbon monoxide</u>. E.g. <u>iron oxide</u> is reduced in an blast furnace to make <u>iron</u>.

2) This is because <u>more reactive elements</u> form compounds more <u>readily</u>. Carbon's more reactive than iron, so carbon 'steals' oxygen from iron oxide (see page 42).

3) In other words, carbon <u>can only take the oxygen</u> away from metals which are <u>less reactive</u> than carbon <u>itself</u> is.

4) Very reactive metals form very <u>stable</u> ores — i.e. it's difficult to get the metal out of its compound. So metals that are <u>more reactive</u> than carbon (they come <u>higher</u> in the <u>reactivity series</u>) have to be extracted using <u>electrolysis</u>. Electrolysis uses <u>electricity</u> to <u>separate the metal</u> from the other elements in the compound (see p.32). For example, aluminium is extracted from <u>aluminium oxide</u> using electrolysis.

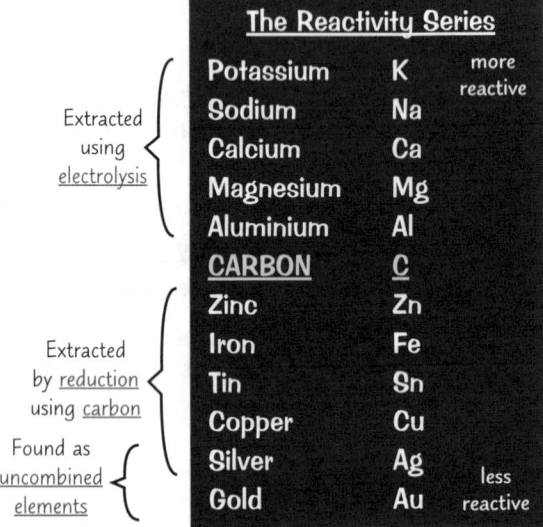

The Reactivity Series

Potassium	K	more reactive
Sodium	Na	
Calcium	Ca	
Magnesium	Mg	
Aluminium	Al	
<u>CARBON</u>	<u>C</u>	
Zinc	Zn	
Iron	Fe	
Tin	Sn	
Copper	Cu	
Silver	Ag	less reactive
Gold	Au	

Extracted using <u>electrolysis</u>

Extracted by <u>reduction</u> using <u>carbon</u>

Found as <u>uncombined</u> <u>elements</u>

The reduction reaction using carbon is a bit like the displacement reactions with the halogens (see page 37).

Paper 2

[Please insert ore-ful pun here]...

Make sure you've got that reactivity series sorted in your head. If a metal's below carbon in the reactivity series, then it's less reactive than carbon and can be extracted from its ore by reduction using carbon. Phew... got it?

Q1 How would you extract tin from its metal ore? Explain your answer. [2 marks]

Uses of Metals

Iron, aluminium and copper are the most produced metals in the whole wide world. Time to learn why.

Iron, Aluminium and Copper have some Properties in Common

Iron, aluminium and copper have the same basic properties — they are all metals after all.

1) They are dense and lustrous (i.e. shiny) and have high melting points — iron melts at 1538 °C, aluminium melts at 660 °C and copper melts at 1085 °C.

2) They have high tensile strength — they're strong and hard to break.

3) But they can also be hammered into a different shape (they're malleable).

4) They are good conductors of electricity and of heat energy too.

There's more on the properties of metals on page 21.

The Uses of Iron, Aluminium and Copper Depend on their Properties

- Iron has all the properties you'd expect a metal to have. Adding other materials to the iron can change its properties though (see below).
- Wrought iron is almost completely pure iron. It's malleable, so it's used to make gates and railings.
- The main problem with iron is that it corrodes easily (i.e. it rusts).

- Aluminium is also a typical metal. However, unlike iron, it doesn't corrode easily.
- The aluminium reacts very quickly with oxygen in the air to form aluminium oxide. A nice protective layer of aluminium oxide sticks firmly to the aluminium below and stops any further reaction taking place.
- Because aluminium doesn't corrode it's useful for products that come in contact with water, e.g. drinks cans — you wouldn't want rust in your fizzy pop.
- Aluminium is also much less dense than iron, which makes it lighter.
- This makes it useful when the weight of the metal is important, e.g. in bicycle frames and aeroplanes.

- Copper is an especially good conductor of heat and electricity.
- It is used in electrical components and wiring as it has low resistance and so is efficient at transferring electricity. It is also used in heating systems, such as underfloor heating, as it allows speedy transfer of heat to the surroundings.

Pure Metals Don't Always Have the Properties Needed

1) The regular structure of pure metals makes them soft — often too soft for use in everyday life.

2) Alloys are made by adding other elements to the metal (usually other metals and/or carbon).

3) Different elements have different sized atoms. So when another element is mixed with a pure metal, the new atoms will distort the layers of metal atoms, making it more difficult for them to slide over each other. This makes alloys harder than pure metals.

TYPE OF STEEL	PROPERTIES	USE
Low carbon steel (0.1–0.3% carbon)	easily shaped	car bodies
High carbon steel (0.22–2.5% carbon)	very strong, inflexible, brittle	bridges
Stainless steel (chromium added, and sometimes nickel)	corrosion-resistant, hard	cutlery

4) Alloys of iron called steels are often used instead of pure iron. Steels are made by adding small amounts of carbon and sometimes other metals to iron.

5) Many other alloys are used in everyday life, e.g. brass (copper + zinc) and bronze (copper + tin).

If Iron Man and the Silver Surfer teamed up, they'd be great alloys...

Life would be pretty different without alloys around. I'd have to cancel my trumpet recital for a start...

Q1   Give one use of steel.   [1 mark]

Paper 2

Acids and Alkalis

To test the pH of a solution, you can use an <u>indicator</u> — and that means <u>colours</u>...

The pH Scale Goes from 0 to 14

1) The <u>strongest acid</u> has <u>pH 0</u>. The <u>strongest alkali</u> has <u>pH 14</u>.
2) A <u>neutral</u> substance has <u>pH 7</u> (e.g. pure water).

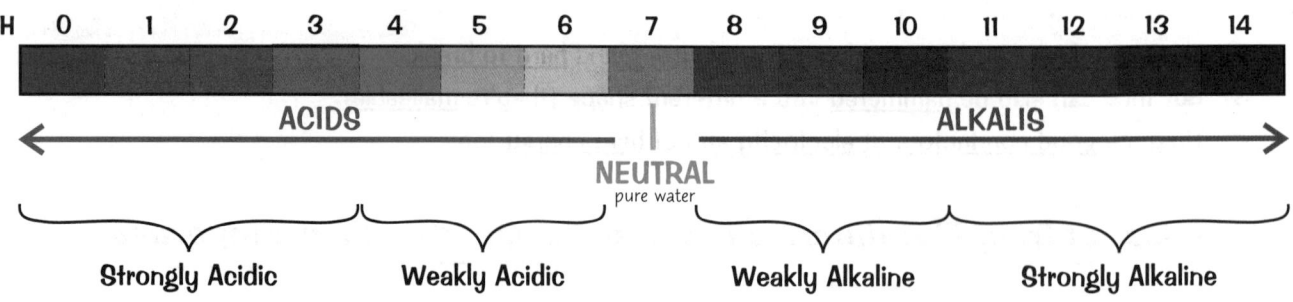

An Indicator is Just a Dye That Changes Colour

The dye in the indicator <u>changes colour</u> depending on whether it's <u>above</u> or <u>below</u> a <u>certain pH</u>.
Indicators are very useful for <u>estimating</u> the pH of a solution. There are several different types:

1) <u>Universal indicator</u> is a very useful <u>combination of dyes</u> which gives the colours shown above.
To find the pH of an <u>aqueous solution</u>, add the indicator to the solution
you are testing and compare the colour formed to a chart.

2) <u>Litmus paper</u> tests whether a solution is acidic or alkaline because
it changes colour at about pH 7. It's <u>red</u> in <u>acidic</u> solutions,
<u>purple</u> in <u>neutral</u> solutions and <u>blue</u> in <u>alkaline</u> solutions.

3) <u>Phenolphthalein</u> will change from <u>colourless</u> in <u>acidic</u> solutions
to <u>bright pink</u> in <u>alkaline</u> solutions.

4) <u>Methyl orange</u> changes from <u>red</u> in <u>acidic</u> solutions to
<u>yellow</u> in <u>alkaline</u> solutions.

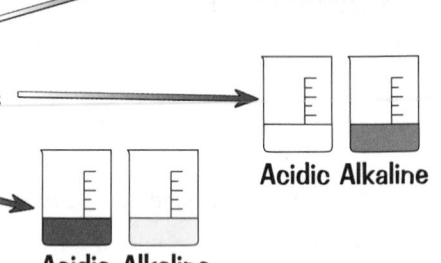

Acids can be Neutralised by Bases (or Alkalis)

An <u>ACID</u> is a source of <u>hydrogen ions</u> (H^+). They are <u>proton donors</u>. Acids have a pH of less than 7.

A <u>BASE</u> is a substance that can neutralise an acid. They are <u>proton acceptors</u>. <u>ALKALIS</u> are
<u>soluble bases</u>. An alkali is a source of <u>hydroxide ions</u> (<u>OH^-</u>) and has a pH greater than 7.

The reaction between an acid and a base (or an acid and an alkali) is called <u>neutralisation</u>.

Neutralisation can be seen in terms of <u>H^+</u> and <u>OH^-</u> <u>ions</u> like this:

$$H^+_{(aq)} + OH^-_{(aq)} \rightarrow H_2O_{(l)}$$

These reactions are sometimes called acid-base reactions.

The reaction can also be seen in terms of <u>proton transfer</u>.
The acid <u>donates</u> protons which are then <u>accepted</u> by the base.

When an acid neutralises a base (or vice versa), the <u>products</u> are <u>neutral</u>, i.e. they have a <u>pH of 7</u>.

This page should have all bases covered...

pHew, you got to the end of the page, so here's an interesting(ish) fact — your skin is slightly acidic (pH 5.5).

Q1   The pH of an unknown solution is found to be 2. Is the solution acidic or alkaline?   [1 mark]

Reactions of Acids

Acids are an enthusiastic bunch — they get involved in loads of reactions.
For example, they can react with <u>metals</u> (see page 41), <u>metal oxides</u> and <u>metal carbonates</u>.

Salts Form When Acids React with Bases

1) A <u>salt</u>, an ionic compound, is formed during a <u>neutralisation reaction</u>
(a reaction between an <u>acid</u> and a <u>base</u>).
This is a general equation for a neutralisation reaction:

> **acid + base → salt + water**

2) The <u>type of salt</u> depends on the <u>acid</u> used. In general, <u>hydrochloric acid</u> produces <u>chloride</u> salts, <u>sulfuric acid</u> produces <u>sulfate salts</u> and <u>nitric acid</u> produces <u>nitrate salts</u>.

3) You need to be able to remember what happens when you add acids to various bases...

Acid + Metal Oxide → Salt + Water

<u>Examples</u>:
$2HCl + CuO → CuCl_2 + H_2O$ (Copper chloride)
$H_2SO_4 + ZnO → ZnSO_4 + H_2O$ (Zinc sulfate)
$2HNO_3 + MgO → Mg(NO_3)_2 + H_2O$ (Magnesium nitrate)

Acid + Metal Hydroxide → Salt + Water

<u>Examples</u>:
$HCl + NaOH → NaCl + H_2O$ (Sodium chloride)
$H_2SO_4 + Zn(OH)_2 → ZnSO_4 + 2H_2O$ (Zinc sulfate)
$HNO_3 + KOH → KNO_3 + H_2O$ (Potassium nitrate)

These are the same as the acid/alkali neutralisation reaction you met on page 46.

Acid + Ammonia → Ammonium Salt

<u>Examples</u>:
$HNO_{3(aq)} + NH_{3(aq)} → NH_4NO_{3(aq)}$ (ammonium nitrate)
$H_2SO_{4(aq)} + 2NH_{3(aq)} → (NH_4)_2SO_{4(aq)}$ (ammonium sulfate)

When ammonia dissolves in water it forms NH_4^+ and OH^- ions. So this reaction is actually:
$NH_4^+ + OH^- + HNO_3 → NH_4NO_3 + H_2O$
as the reactant is aqueous ammonia.

Salts Also Form When Acids React With Metals or Metal Carbonates

You also need to know what happens when you react an <u>acid</u> with a <u>metal</u> or a <u>metal carbonate</u>.
The reaction of acids and metals is covered on page 41 in more detail.

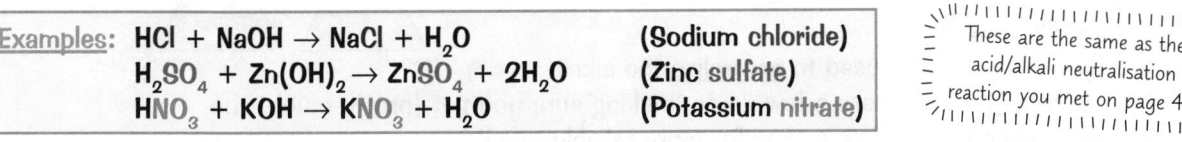

<u>Examples</u>:
$2HCl + Mg → MgCl_2 + H_2$ (Magnesium chloride)
$H_2SO_4 + Mg → MgSO_4 + H_2$ (Magnesium sulfate)

The reaction of nitric acid with metals can be more complicated — you get a nitrate salt, but instead of hydrogen gas, the other products are usually a mixture of water, NO and NO_2.

Acid + Metal Carbonate → Salt + Water + Carbon Dioxide

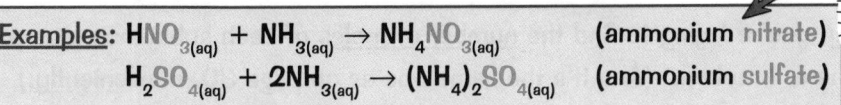

<u>Examples</u>: hydrochloric acid + sodium carbonate → sodium chloride + water + carbon dioxide
$$2HCl + Na_2CO_3 → 2NaCl + H_2O + CO_2$$

sulfuric acid + calcium carbonate → calcium sulfate + water + carbon dioxide
$$H_2SO_4 + CaCO_3 → CaSO_4 + H_2O + CO_2$$

nitric acid + calcium carbonate → calcium nitrate + water + carbon dioxide
$$2HNO_3 + CaCO_3 → Ca(NO_3)_2 + H_2O + CO_2$$

Nitrates — much cheaper than day-rates...

What a lot of reactions. Better take a peek back at page 23 for help with writing and balancing chemical equations.

Q1   Write a balanced chemical equation for the reaction of hydrochloric acid with calcium carbonate.   [2 marks]

Titrations

Titrations have a bad reputation — but they're not as bad as they're made out to be.

Titrations are Used to Find Out Concentrations

1) Titrations allow you to find out exactly how much acid is needed to neutralise a quantity of alkali (or vice versa). Here's how you do a titration...

You can also do titrations the other way round — adding alkali to acid.

2) Using a pipette and pipette filler, add some alkali (usually about 25 cm³) to a conical flask, along with two or three drops of indicator. (The pipette filler stops you getting a mouthful of alkali.)

Pipette
Pipettes measure only one volume of solution. Fill the pipette to about 3 cm above the line, then drop the level down carefully to the line.

Burette
Burettes measure different volumes and let you add the solution drop by drop.

3) Fill a burette with the acid. Make sure you do this BELOW EYE LEVEL — you don't want to be looking up if some acid spills over.

acid

The scale down the side shows the volume of acid used.

4) Using the burette, add the acid to the alkali a bit at a time — giving the conical flask a regular swirl. Go especially slowly when you think the end-point (colour change) is about to be reached.

5) The indicator changes colour when all the alkali has been neutralised, e.g. phenolphthalein is pink in alkalis, but colourless in acids.

Conical flask
containing alkali and indicator.

6) Record the volume of acid used to neutralise the alkali. It's best to repeat this process a few times, making sure you get (pretty much) the same answer each time — this makes for more reliable results.

The Calculation — Work Out the Numbers of Moles

Now for the calculations... basically, you're trying to find the number of moles of each substance (see p.25).

A formula triangle is pretty handy here, I reckon. (And it's the same one as on page 30, conveniently.)

Example: Suppose you start off with 25 cm³ of sodium hydroxide solution in your flask, and you know that its concentration is 0.1 moles per dm³.

You then find from your titration that it takes 30 cm³ of sulfuric acid (of an unknown concentration) to neutralise the sodium hydroxide.

Find the concentration of the acid.

$$\frac{n}{c \times V}$$

moles (mol)

concentration (mol/dm³)

volume (dm³)

Step 1: Work out how many moles of the 'known' substance you have:

Number of moles = concentration × volume = 0.1 × (25 ÷ 1000) = 0.0025 moles

Step 2: Write down the equation for the reaction...

$2NaOH + H_2SO_4 \longrightarrow Na_2SO_4 + 2H_2O$

...and work out how many moles of the 'unknown' stuff you must have had.

Using the equation, you can see that for every two moles of sodium hydroxide you had...
...there was just one mole of sulfuric acid.
So if you had 0.0025 moles of sodium hydroxide...
...you must have had 0.0025 ÷ 2 = 0.00125 moles of sulfuric acid.

Step 3: Work out the concentration of the 'unknown' stuff.

Concentration = number of moles ÷ volume
= 0.00125 ÷ (30 ÷ 1000) = 0.0417 mol/dm³

If you need the concentration in g/dm³, convert your answer using the method on page 30.

Burette and pipettes — big glass things, just waiting to be dropped...

Don't use universal indicator as an indicator in acid-base titrations, it's hard to tell accurately when the reaction is over.

Q1 A 60 cm³ solution of HCl is neutralised by 30 cm³ of 1 mol/dm³ NaOH solution. Calculate the concentration of the HCl in mol/dm³. The equation for the reaction is: HCl + NaOH → NaCl + H₂O [3 marks]

Making Insoluble Salts

Unfortunately for you, you've got to learn which salts are <u>soluble</u> and which ones <u>aren't</u>. Tough luck...

The Rules of Solubility

> Soluble things dissolve in water. Insoluble things don't.

1) How you make a salt depends on whether it's <u>soluble</u> or <u>insoluble</u>.

2) You may need to work out if, when two solutions are mixed, a salt will form as a <u>precipitate</u> (i.e. it's an insoluble salt), or whether it will just form <u>in solution</u> (i.e. it's a soluble salt).

3) This table is a pretty fail-safe way of working out whether a substance is soluble in water or not.

Substance	Soluble or Insoluble?
common salts of sodium, potassium and ammonium	soluble
nitrates	soluble
common chlorides	soluble (except silver chloride and lead chloride)
common sulfates	soluble (except lead, barium and calcium sulfate)
common carbonates	insoluble (except for sodium, potassium and ammonium ones)
common hydroxides	insoluble (except for sodium, potassium and calcium ones)

Making Insoluble Salts — Precipitation Reactions

1) To make a pure, dry sample of an <u>insoluble</u> salt, you can use a <u>precipitation reaction</u>. You just need to pick the right two <u>soluble salts</u> and <u>react</u> them together to get your <u>insoluble salt</u>.

2) E.g. to make <u>lead sulfate</u> (insoluble), mix <u>lead nitrate</u> and <u>magnesium sulfate</u> (both soluble).

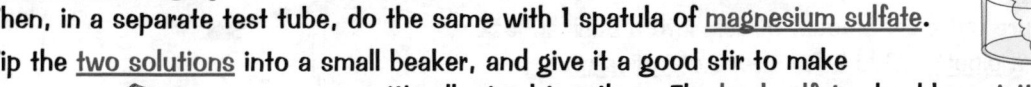

lead nitrate + magnesium sulfate → lead sulfate + magnesium nitrate

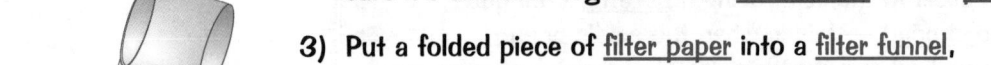

$$Pb(NO_3)_{2\,(aq)} + MgSO_{4(aq)} \rightarrow PbSO_{4\,(s)} + Mg(NO_3)_{2\,(aq)}$$

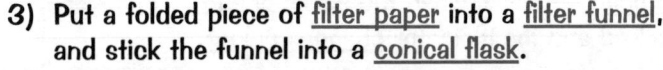

Making Lead Sulfate

PRACTICAL

1) Add 1 spatula of <u>lead nitrate</u> to a test tube. Add <u>water</u> to dissolve it. You should use deionised water to make sure there are no other ions about. <u>Shake it thoroughly</u> to ensure that all the lead nitrate has <u>dissolved</u>. Then, in a separate test tube, do the same with 1 spatula of <u>magnesium sulfate</u>.

precipitate

2) Tip the <u>two solutions</u> into a small beaker, and give it a good stir to make sure it's all mixed together. The <u>lead sulfate</u> should <u>precipitate</u> out.

filter paper

filter funnel

3) Put a folded piece of <u>filter paper</u> into a <u>filter funnel</u>, and stick the funnel into a <u>conical flask</u>.

4) <u>Pour</u> the contents of the beaker into the middle of the filter paper. Make sure that the solution doesn't go above the filter paper — otherwise some of the solid could dribble down the side.

5) <u>Swill out</u> the beaker with more deionised water, and tip this into the filter paper — to make sure you get <u>all the precipitate</u> from the beaker.

6) Rinse the contents of the filter paper with deionised water to make sure that <u>all the soluble magnesium nitrate</u> has been washed away.

lead sulfate

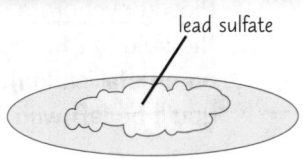

7) Then just scrape the <u>lead sulfate</u> onto fresh filter paper and leave it to dry in an oven or a desiccator.

Lead sulfate just doesn't behave — it's an intolerable salt...

The theory may seem dull, but you'll probably get to make some nice salts in your class, and that's pretty cool.

Q1 State whether the following salts are soluble or insoluble:
a) potassium chloride b) copper carbonate c) calcium sulfate d) sodium hydroxide [4 marks]

Making Soluble Salts

You met the technique for making <u>insoluble salts</u> on the last page. Time for <u>soluble salts</u> now...

Making Soluble Salts — Use an Acid and an Insoluble Base

PRACTICAL

1) You can make a <u>soluble salt</u> by reacting an <u>acid</u> that contains one of the ions you want in the salt with an <u>insoluble base</u> that contains the other ion you need (often a <u>metal oxide</u> or <u>metal hydroxide</u>).

For some salts, you can use a <u>metal</u> instead of the base.

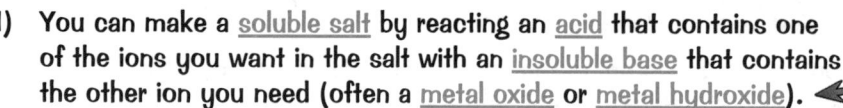

filter paper
filter funnel
excess solid
salt and water

2) Start by <u>heating the acid</u> in a <u>water bath</u> — this speeds up the reaction between the acid and the insoluble base. Do this in a <u>fume cupboard</u> to avoid releasing acid fumes into the room.

3) Then add the <u>base</u> to the <u>acid</u> — the base and acid will react to produce a <u>soluble salt</u> (and water). You will know when the base is in excess and all the acid has been neutralised because the excess solid will just <u>sink</u> to the bottom of the flask.
(It's important that the base is in excess so that you don't have any leftover acid in your product.)

4) <u>Filter</u> off the <u>excess</u> solid to get a solution containing only the <u>salt</u> and <u>water</u>.

5) <u>Heat the solution gently</u>, using a Bunsen burner, to slowly <u>evaporate</u> off some of the water. Leave the solution to cool and allow the salt to <u>crystallise</u> (see p.9). Filter off the <u>solid salt</u> and leave it to <u>dry</u>.

> <u>Example:</u> You can add <u>copper oxide</u> to warm <u>sulfuric acid</u> to make a solution of <u>copper sulfate</u>:
> $$CuO_{(s)} + H_2SO_{4\,(aq)} \rightarrow CuSO_{4\,(aq)} + H_2O_{(l)}$$
> If you evaporate off some of the water and leave this solution to <u>crystallise</u>, you should get lovely <u>blue crystals</u> of <u>hydrated copper sulfate</u>, which you can <u>filter off</u> and <u>dry</u>.

You can Make Soluble Salts Using Acid/Alkali Reactions

1) Soluble salts (salts that dissolve in water) can be made by reacting an acid with an <u>alkali</u>.

2) But you can't tell whether the reaction has <u>finished</u> — there's no signal that all the acid has been neutralised. You also can't just add an <u>excess</u> of alkali to the acid, because the salt is <u>soluble</u> and would be contaminated with the excess alkali.

3) Instead, you need to work out <u>exactly</u> the right amount of alkali to <u>neutralise</u> the acid. For this, you need to do a <u>titration</u> using an <u>indicator</u>. Here's what you do...

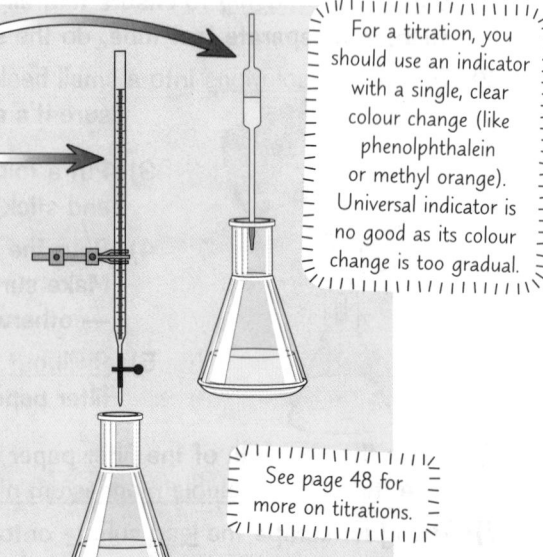

- Measure out a set amount of acid into a conical flask using a <u>pipette</u>. Add a few drops of <u>indicator</u>.
- Slowly add alkali to the acid, using a <u>burette</u>, until you reach the <u>end point</u> — this is when the acid's been exactly neutralised and the indicator <u>changes colour</u>.
- Then, carry out the reaction using exactly the same volumes of alkali and acid but with no <u>indicator</u>, so the salt <u>won't be contaminated</u> with indicator.
- The <u>solution</u> that remains when the reaction is complete contains only the <u>salt</u> and <u>water</u>.
- Slowly <u>evaporate</u> off some of the water and then leave the solution to crystallise (see page 9 for more on crystallisation). Filter off the solid and dry it — you'll be left with a <u>pure</u>, <u>dry</u> salt.

For a titration, you should use an indicator with a single, clear colour change (like phenolphthalein or methyl orange). Universal indicator is no good as its colour change is too gradual.

See page 48 for more on titrations.

I was attacked by a nasty copper sulfate — it was a-salt...

Yet more salts for you to make. If I were you though, I'd just get my salts from a sachet at the local chippy...

Q1 Iron nitrate is a soluble salt that can be made from iron oxide (an insoluble base) and nitric acid. Suggest a method you could use to make a pure sample of iron nitrate from these reactants. [5 marks]

Tests for Cations

So, tests for identifying cations in mystery compounds probably don't get your heart racing with excitement, but this section includes lots of different colours so just think of all the pretty revision notes you could make...

Flame Tests Identify Metal Ions

Compounds of some metals burn with a characteristic colour (as you see every November 5th).

So you can test for various metal ions by heating your substance and seeing whether it burns with a distinctive colour flame.

Lithium, Li^+, burns with a red flame.

Sodium, Na^+, burns with a yellow flame.

Potassium, K^+, burns with a lilac flame.

Calcium, Ca^{2+}, burns with an orange-red flame.

Copper ions, Cu^{2+}, give a blue-green flame.

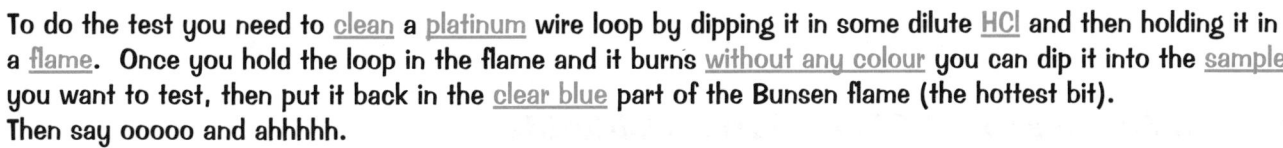

To do the test you need to clean a platinum wire loop by dipping it in some dilute HCl and then holding it in a flame. Once you hold the loop in the flame and it burns without any colour you can dip it into the sample you want to test, then put it back in the clear blue part of the Bunsen flame (the hottest bit). Then say ooooo and ahhhhh.

Some Metals Form a Coloured Precipitate with NaOH

This is also a test for metal ions, but it's slightly more involved. Concentrate now...

1) Many metal hydroxides are insoluble and precipitate out of solution when formed. Some of these hydroxides have a characteristic colour.

2) So in this test you add a few drops of sodium hydroxide solution to a solution of your mystery compound in a test tube — all in the hope of forming an insoluble hydroxide.

3) If you get a coloured insoluble hydroxide you can then tell which metal was in the compound.

Metal ion	Colour of precipitate	Ionic Reaction
Copper(II), Cu^{2+}	Blue	$Cu^{2+}_{(aq)} + 2OH^-_{(aq)} \rightarrow Cu(OH)_{2\,(s)}$
Iron(II), Fe^{2+}	Sludgy green	$Fe^{2+}_{(aq)} + 2OH^-_{(aq)} \rightarrow Fe(OH)_{2\,(s)}$
Iron(III), Fe^{3+}	Reddish brown	$Fe^{3+}_{(aq)} + 3OH^-_{(aq)} \rightarrow Fe(OH)_{3\,(s)}$

"Ammonium Compound + NaOH" Gives Off (Stinky) Ammonia

1) Ammonia gas (NH_3) is smelly — it reeks of cat wee. You can usually tell if there's some about, but it's not a good idea to smell it deliberately as it can be really harmful to your eyes — not cool.

2) You can check for ammonia gas using a damp piece of red litmus paper. If there's ammonia present, the paper will turn blue. → weak alkali

3) You can use this to test whether a substance contains ammonium ions (NH_4^+). Add some sodium hydroxide to a solution of your mystery substance in a test tube. If there's ammonia given off this means there are ammonium ions in your mystery substance.

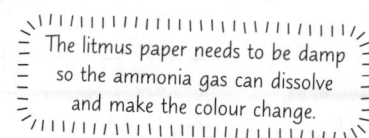
The litmus paper needs to be damp so the ammonia gas can dissolve and make the colour change.

Cations — ions with a pawsitive charge...

Lots of ions and colours to learn here, so just take your time. I like to remember Li̱ttle Red Riding Hood.

Q1   A compound is heated in a flame. A lilac flame is produced. What does this show?   [1 mark]

Q2   A few drops of sodium hydroxide are added to an unknown solution.
        A red-brown precipitate forms. What does this tell you about the solution?   [1 mark]

Tests for Anions

It's not just positive ions you can test for, you'll be pleased to know.
Yep, you can also test for <u>negative ions</u>. So the fun goes on...

Hydrochloric Acid Can Help Detect Carbonates

To <u>test for carbonates</u>, add dilute <u>hydrochloric acid</u> (HCl) to your test sample.
If <u>carbonates</u> (CO_3^{2-}) are present then <u>carbon dioxide</u> will be released.

> **Carbonates give off CO_2 with HCl**

> carbonate + acid → carbon dioxide + water
> $$CO_3^{2-}{}_{(s)} + 2H^+{}_{(aq)} \rightarrow CO_2{}_{(g)} + H_2O_{(l)}$$

You can test for carbon dioxide using <u>limewater</u> — see next page.

Anne irons.

Test for Sulfates with HCl and Barium Chloride

> **Sulfate ions (SO_4^{2-}) produce a white precipitate**

To test for a <u>sulfate</u> ion (SO_4^{2-}), add <u>dilute HCl</u>, followed by <u>barium chloride solution</u>, $BaCl_2$.

> $$Ba^{2+}{}_{(aq)} + SO_4^{2-}{}_{(aq)} \rightarrow BaSO_4{}_{(s)}$$
> barium ions + sulfate ions → barium sulfate

A <u>white precipitate</u> of <u>barium sulfate</u> means the original compound was a sulfate.

(The <u>hydrochloric acid</u> is added to get rid of any traces of <u>carbonate</u> or <u>sulfite</u> ions before you do the test.
Both of these would also produce a precipitate, so they'd <u>confuse</u> the results.)

Test for Halides (Cl⁻, Br⁻, I⁻) with Nitric Acid and Silver Nitrate

To test for <u>chloride</u>, <u>bromide</u> or <u>iodide</u> ions, add dilute <u>nitric acid</u> (HNO_3),
followed by <u>silver nitrate solution</u> ($AgNO_3$).

$$Ag^+{}_{(aq)} + Cl^-{}_{(aq)} \longrightarrow AgCl_{(s)}$$ A <u>chloride</u> ion gives a **white** precipitate of <u>silver chloride</u>.

$$Ag^+{}_{(aq)} + Br^-{}_{(aq)} \longrightarrow AgBr_{(s)}$$ A <u>bromide</u> ion gives a **cream** precipitate of <u>silver bromide</u>.

$$Ag^+{}_{(aq)} + I^-{}_{(aq)} \longrightarrow AgI_{(s)}$$ An <u>iodide</u> ion gives a **yellow** precipitate of <u>silver iodide</u>.

(Again, the <u>acid</u> is added to get rid of <u>carbonate</u> or <u>sulfite</u> ions before the test.
You use <u>nitric acid</u> in this test, though, <u>not HCl</u>.)

Chop them and see if you cry — oh wait, you said test for anions...

Unfortunately, the colours here aren't quite as exciting as those in the tests for cations but they are just as important...

Q1   A chemist adds some dilute nitric acid to a solution, X, followed by some silver nitrate solution.
     A yellow precipitate forms. What does this tell the chemist about solution X?   [1 mark]

Tests for Gases and Water

There are lots of clever ways of testing for <u>different gases</u>. But dipping your finger in a liquid and saying "<u>it's wet</u>" is <u>not</u> the best test for water. Don't worry though, there's a more scientific method for that too...

There are Tests for 5 Common Gases

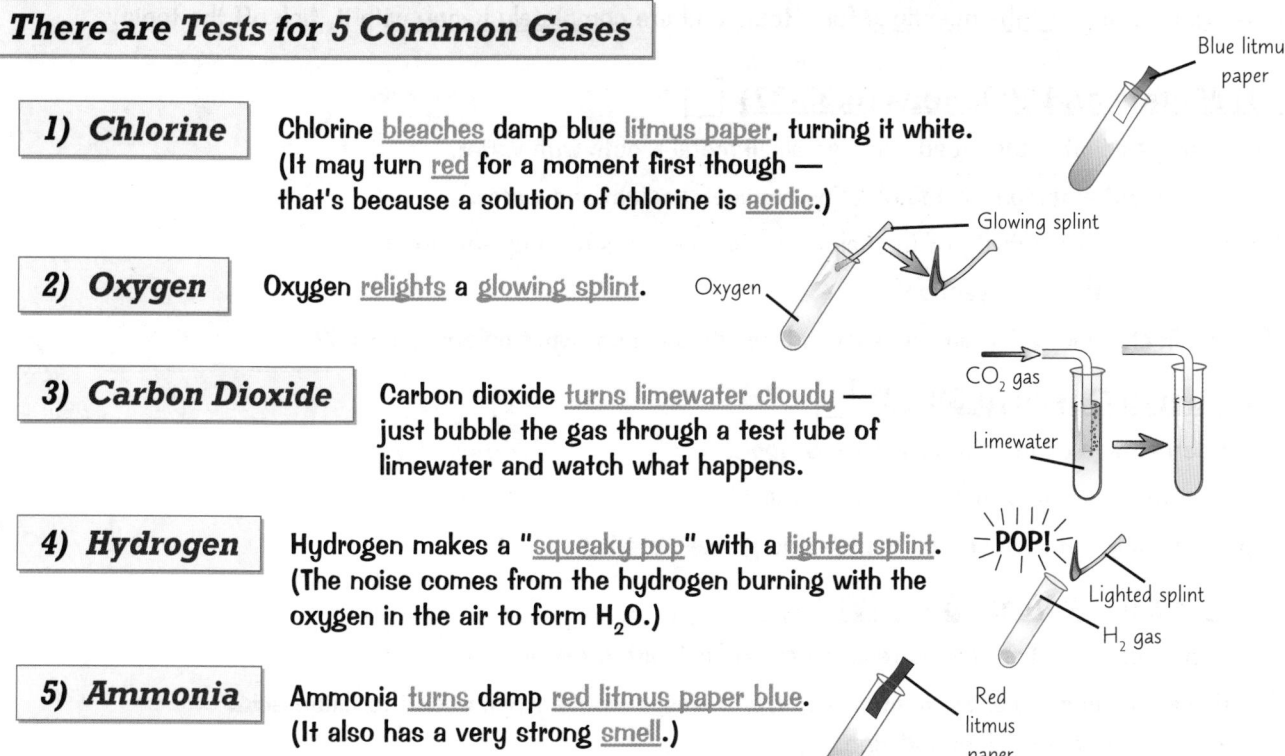

1) Chlorine   Chlorine <u>bleaches</u> damp blue <u>litmus paper</u>, turning it white. (It may turn <u>red</u> for a moment first though — that's because a solution of chlorine is <u>acidic</u>.)

Blue litmus paper

2) Oxygen   Oxygen <u>relights</u> a <u>glowing splint</u>.

Glowing splint

Oxygen

3) Carbon Dioxide   Carbon dioxide <u>turns limewater cloudy</u> — just bubble the gas through a test tube of limewater and watch what happens.

CO_2 gas

Limewater

4) Hydrogen   Hydrogen makes a "<u>squeaky pop</u>" with a <u>lighted splint</u>. (The noise comes from the hydrogen burning with the oxygen in the air to form H_2O.)

POP!

Lighted splint

H_2 gas

5) Ammonia   Ammonia <u>turns</u> damp <u>red litmus paper blue</u>. (It also has a very strong <u>smell</u>.)

Red litmus paper

Wet Copper(II) Sulfate is Blue — Dry Copper(II) Sulfate is White

<u>Copper(II) sulfate</u> crystals can be used as a <u>test</u> for <u>water</u>.

1) When copper(II) sulfate is <u>bound to water</u> (water of crystallisation, see page 29) it forms lovely <u>blue crystals</u>.

2) If you <u>heat</u> the <u>blue hydrated</u> copper(II) sulfate crystals it drives the water off.

3) This leaves a <u>white anhydrous</u> copper(II) sulfate powder, which <u>doesn't</u> have any water bound to it.

Water vapour

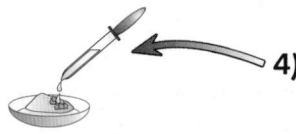

4) If you then <u>add</u> a couple of drops of <u>water</u> to the <u>white powder</u> you get the <u>blue crystals</u> back again.

Hydrated means with water. Anhydrous means without water.

So, if you want to <u>test for water</u>, all you need to do is add <u>anhydrous copper(II) sulfate</u> and see if the white powder turns blue.

This test <u>will</u> tell you if water is <u>present</u> in a solution but it <u>won't</u> tell you if the water is <u>pure</u>.

- When a sample is <u>pure</u> it means it's only made up of <u>one substance</u>.
- This means it has set <u>defined physical properties</u> like <u>boiling point</u> and <u>freezing point</u>.

<u>Pure water</u> will always: **Boil at 100 °C**

                                         Freeze at 0 °C

If you find the boiling point isn't 100 °C or freezing point isn't 0 °C then the sample <u>isn't pure</u>.

Hopefully this page won't be too testing for you...

How to learn this page — don't stare at the whole thing till your eyes swim and you don't want to see the word 'litmus' ever again. Each test has been given its own section, so take them one by one and learn it that way.

Q1   A reaction produces ammonia gas. Describe how you would test for this gas.   [1 mark]

Section 4 — Inorganic Chemistry

Revision Questions for Section 4

Well, that wraps up <u>Section 4</u> — time to test your mettle (pun intended) on some revision questions.

- Try these questions and <u>tick off each one</u> when you <u>get it right</u>.
- When you've done <u>all the questions</u> for a topic and are <u>completely happy</u> with it, tick off the topic.

<u>Alkali Metals and Halogens (p.35-37)</u> ☑

1) Name the gas that is produced when an alkali metal reacts with water.
2) Write the word equation for the reaction between sodium and water.
3) Describe how the reactivity of the halogens changes as you go up the group.
4) What is a displacement reaction?
5) If you mix chlorine water with potassium bromide solution, what colour will it go?

<u>Atmospheric Gases (p.38-40)</u> ☐

6) What percentage of the atmosphere is oxygen?
7) Describe the reaction of oxygen with magnesium.
8) Explain the link between carbon dioxide and global warming.

<u>Metals and their Uses (p.41-45)</u> ☐

9) Write the word equation for the reaction of an acid with a metal.
10) Put these metals in order from most reactive to least reactive when added to dilute acid:
    aluminium, iron, magnesium and zinc.
11) Give the name of: a) a very reactive metal, b) a not at all reactive metal.
12) What happens when a more reactive metal is put in a solution of a less reactive metal salt?
13) Describe two ways that rusting can be prevented.
14) Are metal oxides reduced or oxidised to obtain the metal from them?
    What role does carbon play in the reduction of a metal oxide with a less reactive metal?
15) What method of extraction would you use for a) magnesium, b) iron?
16) Name an element that can be added to iron to make steel.

<u>Acids and Alkalis (p.46-48)</u> ☐

17) What colour will methyl orange be in alkaline solutions?
18) What two products form when a metal oxide reacts with an acid?
19) Why should you carry out a titration multiple times?

<u>Making Salts (p.49-50)</u> ☑

20) List three insoluble sulfates.
21) Name two soluble hydroxides.
22) Describe how you could make a pure sample of a soluble salt from an acid and an alkali.

<u>Chemical Tests (p.51-53)</u> ☑

23) What colour flame does copper burn with?
24) What colour precipitate do iron(II) compounds form with sodium hydroxide?
25) What colour is the precipitate formed when a bromide ion reacts with dilute nitric acid and silver nitrate?
26) What is the test for hydrogen gas?
27) How can you tell if a sample of water is pure?

Energy Transfer in Reactions

So, endothermic and exothermic reactions are all about taking in and giving out energy to the surroundings.
I think endothermic reactions are a bit self centred really — they just take, take, take...

Combustion reactions (where something burns in oxygen — see page 72) are always exothermic.

Reactions are Exothermic or Endothermic

An **EXOTHERMIC** reaction is one which gives out energy to the surroundings, usually in the form of heat and usually shown by a rise in temperature of the surroundings.

An **ENDOTHERMIC** reaction is one which takes in energy from the surroundings, usually in the form of heat and usually shown by a fall in temperature of the surroundings.

The Change in Energy is Called the Enthalpy Change

The overall change in energy in a reaction is called the **ENTHALPY** change. It has the symbol ΔH.

Δ is the Greek letter 'delta'. It means 'change in'. The H means enthalpy.

1) The units of ΔH are kJ/mol — so it's the amount of energy in kilojoules per mole of reactant.
2) Enthalpy change can have a positive value or a negative value.
   • If the reaction is exothermic, the value is negative because the reaction is giving out energy.
   • If the reaction is endothermic, the value is positive because the reaction takes in energy.

Reaction Profiles Show Energy Changes

Reaction profiles are sometimes called energy level diagrams.

Reaction profiles are diagrams that show the relative energies of the reactants and products in a reaction, and how the energy changes over the course of the reaction.

1) This shows an exothermic reaction — the products are at a lower energy than the reactants. The difference in height represents the energy given out (per mole) in the reaction. ΔH is negative here.

2) The initial rise in energy represents the energy needed to start the reaction. This is the activation energy (E_a).

3) The activation energy is the minimum amount of energy the reactants need to collide with each other and react.

EXOTHERMIC

Energy | Activation Energy | Reactants | Energy released -ve ΔH | Products
Progress of Reaction

There's more on activation energy and collision theory on page 59.

1) This shows an endothermic reaction because the products are at a higher energy than the reactants.

2) The difference in height represents the energy taken in (per mole) during the reaction. ΔH is positive here.

ENDOTHERMIC

Energy | Activation energy | Products | Energy absorbed +ve ΔH | Reactants
Progress of Reaction

Energy transfer — make sure you take it all in...

Remember, "exo-" = exit, "-thermic" = heat, so an exothermic reaction is one that gives out heat (and warms its surroundings) — and endothermic means just the opposite. Once you've got that firmly in your noggin, read on...

Q1   Here is the equation for the combustion of methane in air: $CH_{4(g)} + 2O_{2(g)} \rightarrow CO_{2(g)} + 2H_2O_{(g)}$
      Draw a reaction profile for this reaction.   [3 marks]

PRACTICAL Measuring Enthalpy Changes

Did you know that you can actually <u>measure</u> all this enthalpy stuff in the lab... oh yes, read on...

You Can Find Out Enthalpy Changes Using Calorimetry

<u>Calorimetry</u> allows you to measure the amount of <u>energy transferred</u> in a <u>chemical reaction</u> with a pretty simple set of equipment. Here are two different types of experiment you can do:

Calorimetry — Dissolving, Displacement and Neutralisation Reactions

To measure the amount of <u>energy transferred</u> in these <u>reactions</u> (in solution) you just take the <u>temperature of the reactants</u> (making sure they're the same), <u>mix</u> them and measure the <u>temperature of the solution</u> at the <u>end</u> of the reaction. Easy.

1) So if you want to investigate the enthalpy change of <u>dissolving</u>, <u>displacement</u> (see page 37) or <u>neutralisation</u> reactions (see page 47) you can do it by mixing the reactants in a <u>polystyrene cup</u> (very technical).

2) The biggest <u>problem</u> with energy measurements is the amount of energy <u>lost to the surroundings</u>.

3) You can reduce it a bit by putting the polystyrene cup into a <u>beaker of cotton wool</u> to give <u>more insulation</u>, and putting a <u>lid</u> on the cup to reduce energy lost by <u>evaporation</u>.

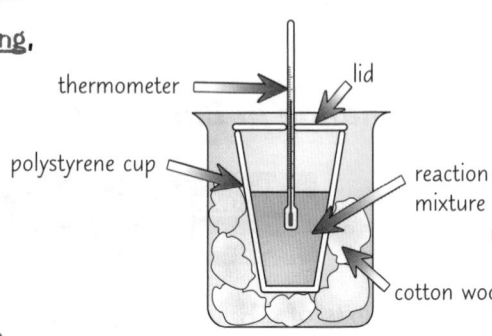

thermometer
lid
polystyrene cup
reaction mixture
cotton wool

4) Here's how you could measure the energy transferred in a <u>neutralisation</u> reaction between hydrochloric acid (HCl) and sodium hydroxide (NaOH):

1) Put 25 cm³ of hydrochloric acid and sodium hydroxide in <u>separate beakers</u>.
2) Place the beakers in a water bath set to 25 °C until they are both at the <u>same temperature</u> (25 °C).
3) Add the HCl followed by the NaOH to a polystyrene cup with a lid — as in the diagram above.
4) Take the temperature of the mixture <u>every 30 seconds</u>, and record the highest temperature.

Calorimetry — Combustion

To measure the amount of energy transferred when a fuel is burnt, you can simply burn the fuel and use the flame to <u>heat up some water</u>. This method uses a <u>metal container</u>, usually made of <u>copper</u> because copper conducts heat so well.

1) It's dead important to make as much heat as possible go into <u>heating up</u> the water. <u>Reducing draughts</u> is the key here — use a <u>screen</u> to act as a draught excluder (and don't do it next to an open window).

2) Put 50 g of water in the copper can and <u>record its temperature</u>.

3) <u>Weigh the spirit burner</u> and lid.

4) Put the spirit burner underneath the can, and light the wick. Heat the water, <u>stirring constantly</u>, until the temperature reaches about <u>50 °C</u>.

5) <u>Put out the flame</u> using the burner lid, and measure the <u>final temperature</u> of the water.

6) <u>Weigh</u> the spirit burner and lid <u>again</u>.

7) You can then use the measurements you've taken to <u>calculate the enthalpy change</u> — see the next page.

thermometer
lid
copper can
50 cm³ water
draught excluder
spirit burner

I like my experiments how I like my coffee — in a polystyrene cup...

Just the two experimental methods to learn from this page. Make sure you know which set-up you would use for which type of reaction, and how to stop energy being lost to the surroundings.

Q1 The energy change measured in a calorimetry experiment is always less than the total energy transferred during the experiment. Suggest the reason why. [1 mark]

Calculating Enthalpy Changes

If you've read the previous page, you'll know how to get <u>temperature measurements</u> from the start and end of reactions and to work out how much <u>fuel</u> was used for combustion. Now it's calculations time... woo...

Calculate the Heat Energy Transferred

1) The <u>combustion</u> experiment on the previous page involves <u>heating water</u> by burning a <u>liquid fuel</u>.

2) If you measure (i) <u>how much fuel</u> you've burned and (ii) the <u>temperature change</u> of the water, you can work out how much energy is supplied by <u>each gram of fuel</u>. You need this equation:

heat energy transferred (J) —

mass of liquid being heated (g) —

$$Q = m \times c \times \Delta T$$

— change in temperature of the liquid (°C)

— specific heat capacity (J/g/°C)

3) You also need to know water's <u>specific heat capacity</u> — this is the <u>amount of energy</u> needed to raise the temperature of <u>1 gram</u> of water by <u>1 °C</u>. The specific heat capacity of <u>water</u> is <u>4.2 J/g/°C</u> — so it takes 4.2 joules of energy to raise the temperature of 1 g of water by 1 °C.

<u>Example: to work out the heat energy change per gram of methylated spirit (meths):</u>

Temperature of water in copper can before heating = 21.5 °C
Temperature of water in copper can after heating = 52.5 °C

⟹ Temperature rise of 50 g of water due to heating = <u>31.0 °C</u>

Using the equation, Q = m × c × ΔT,

⟶ You'll be given this value in the exam.

the heat <u>energy transferred</u> in this experiment = 50 × 4.2 × 31 = 6510 joules.

Mass of spirit burner + lid before heating = 68.75 g
Mass of spirit burner + lid after heating = 67.85 g

⟹ Mass of meths burnt = <u>0.90 g</u>

So 0.90 g of meths produces 6510 joules of energy...
...meaning 1 g of meths produces 6510/0.90 = <u>7230 J</u> or <u>7.23 kJ</u>

Energy's wasted heating the can, air, etc. So this figure will often be much lower than the <u>actual</u> energy content.

Calculate the Molar Enthalpy Change

Once you've calculated the <u>heat energy change</u> (Q) you can use it to work out the <u>molar enthalpy change, ΔH</u> (the enthalpy change given out by one mole of the reactant). See page 25 for more on moles. You need the <u>same info</u> as before and the <u>M_r</u> of the fuel (see page 24).

<u>Example: to work out the energy per mole of methylated spirit (meths):</u>

① First, calculate the <u>heat energy change</u> (Q).
From the calculation above, we know the energy transferred in this experiment = 6510 J or 6.51 kJ

② Next, you need to find <u>how many moles of fuel</u> produced this energy change. The M_r of meths is 44.6.
It's back to the old number of moles = $\dfrac{\text{mass (g)}}{M_r}$ equation. So, number of moles = $\dfrac{0.90}{44.6}$ = 0.020 moles

③ So, the <u>heat transferred by 1 mole</u> of fuel (ΔH) = $\dfrac{-6.51}{0.020}$ = –325.5 kJ/mol

The sign has changed to <u>negative</u> because combustion is an <u>exothermic</u> reaction.

Get this right in the exam and you might be as happy as this cowboy.

AHHHHHHHHHHHHH — calculations...

They're not that bad once you get your head around them — just make sure you remember the steps and the formulas.

Q1   A student burns a fuel to heat 40 g of water. The temperature of the water increases by 26 °C.
    Calculate the energy transferred in this reaction. (The specific heat capacity of water is 4.2 J/g/°C.) [2 marks]

Bond Energies

You can <u>calculate</u> the <u>enthalpy change</u> for a reaction by looking at the bonds that are made and broken.

Energy Must Always be Supplied to Break Bonds

There's more on energy transfer on page 55.

1) During a chemical reaction, <u>old bonds are broken</u> and <u>new bonds are formed</u>.

2) Energy must be <u>supplied</u> to break <u>existing bonds</u> — so bond breaking is an <u>endothermic</u> process.

3) Energy is <u>released</u> when new bonds are <u>formed</u> — so bond formation is an <u>exothermic</u> process.

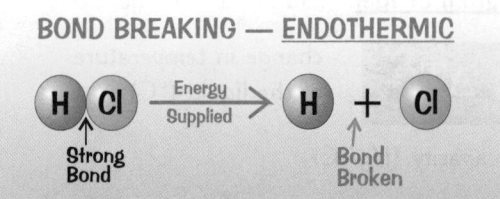

BOND BREAKING — <u>ENDOTHERMIC</u>

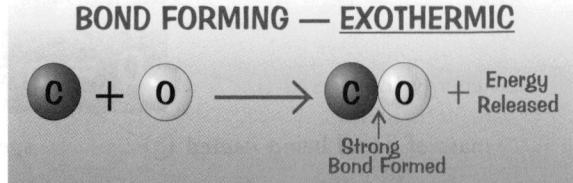

BOND FORMING — <u>EXOTHERMIC</u>

4) In <u>endothermic</u> reactions, the energy <u>used</u> to break bonds is <u>greater</u> than the energy <u>released</u> by forming them.

5) In <u>exothermic</u> reactions, the energy <u>released</u> by forming bonds is <u>greater</u> than the energy used to <u>break</u> 'em.

Bond Energy Calculations — Need to be Practised

1) <u>Each type</u> of chemical bond (e.g. C–C or C–H) has a particular <u>bond energy</u> associated with it.

2) This <u>bond energy</u> can vary slightly depending on what <u>compound</u> the bond is in — so you'll be given <u>average bond energies</u> in the exam.

3) You can use these to calculate the <u>enthalpy</u> change for a reaction. The basic idea is really simple — add up the energy of the bonds that are <u>broken</u> and <u>subtract</u> the energy of the bonds that are <u>made</u>.

$$\text{Enthalpy change } (\Delta H) = \text{Total energy absorbed to break bonds} - \text{Total energy released in making bonds}$$

4) A <u>positive</u> energy change means an <u>endothermic</u> reaction and a <u>negative</u> energy change means an <u>exothermic</u> reaction.

5) You need to <u>practise</u> a few of these, but the basic idea is really very simple...

> <u>Example:</u> Using the bond energy values below, calculate the enthalpy change for the following reaction, where hydrogen and chlorine react to produce hydrogen chloride:
>
> $$H—H + Cl—Cl \rightarrow 2H—Cl$$
>
> H—H: 436 kJ/mol   Cl—Cl: 242 kJ/mol   H—Cl: 431 kJ/mol
>
> 1) Work out the energy required to break the <u>original bonds</u> in the reactants.
> $(1 \times H—H) + (1 \times Cl—Cl) = 436 + 242$
> $= 678$ kJ/mol
>
> 2) Work out the energy released by forming the <u>new bonds</u> in the products.
> $(2 \times H—Cl) = 2 \times 431$
> $= 862$ kJ/mol
>
> 3) Work out the enthalpy change.
> $\Delta H = 678 - 862 = -184$ kJ/mol
>
> *In this reaction, the energy released by forming bonds is greater than the energy used to break them so the reaction is exothermic.*

A student and their mobile — a bond that can never be broken...

This stuff might look hard at the moment, but with a bit of practice it's dead easy and it'll win you easy marks if you understand all the theory behind it. See how you get on with this question:

Q1 N_2 reacts with H_2 in the following reaction: $N_2 + 3H_2 \rightarrow 2NH_3$
The bond energies for these molecules are:
N≡N: 941 kJ/mol
H–H: 436 kJ/mol
N–H: 391 kJ/mol
Calculate the enthalpy change for the reaction.   [3 marks]

N≡N + H–H + H–H + H–H ⟶ (NH₃) + (NH₃)

Rates of Reaction

Rates of reaction are pretty <u>important</u>. In the <u>chemical industry</u>, the <u>faster</u> you make <u>chemicals</u>, the <u>faster</u> you make <u>money</u> (and the faster everyone gets to go home for tea).

Reactions Can Go at All Sorts of Different Rates

1) The <u>rate</u> of a chemical reaction is how fast the <u>reactants</u> are <u>changed</u> into <u>products</u>.

2) One of the <u>slowest</u> is the rusting of iron (it's not slow enough though — what about my little Mini).

3) An example of a <u>moderate speed</u> reaction would be the metal <u>magnesium</u> reacting with an <u>acid</u> to produce a gentle stream of bubbles.

4) <u>Burning</u> is a <u>fast</u> reaction, but <u>explosions</u> are even <u>faster</u> and release a lot of gas. Explosive reactions are all over in a <u>fraction of a second</u>.

You Need to Understand Graphs for the Rate of Reaction

1) You can find the speed of a reaction by recording the amount of <u>product formed</u>, or the amount of <u>reactant used up</u> over <u>time</u> (see page 62).

2) The <u>steeper</u> the line on the graph, the <u>faster</u> the rate of reaction. <u>Over time</u> the line becomes <u>less steep</u> as the reactants are <u>used up</u>.

3) The <u>quickest reactions</u> have the <u>steepest</u> lines and become <u>flat</u> in the <u>least time</u>.

4) The plot below uses the amount of <u>product formed</u> over time to show how the <u>speed</u> of a particular reaction varies under <u>different conditions</u>.

For more on the conditions that affect the rate of reaction — see next page.

- Graph 1 represents the <u>original reaction</u>.

- Graphs 2 and 3 represent the reaction taking place <u>quicker</u>, but with the <u>same initial amounts</u> of reactants. The slopes of the graphs are <u>steeper</u> than for graph 1.

- Graphs 1, 2 and 3 all converge at the <u>same level</u>, showing that they all produce the <u>same amount</u> of product although they take <u>different times</u> to produce it.

- Graph 4 shows <u>more product</u> and a <u>faster reaction</u>. This can only happen if <u>more reactant(s)</u> are added at the start.

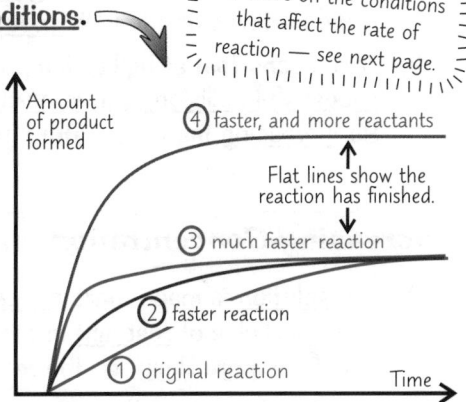

Amount of product formed

④ faster, and more reactants

Flat lines show the reaction has finished.

③ much faster reaction

② faster reaction

① original reaction

Time

Particles Must Collide with Enough Energy in Order to React

Reaction rates are explained perfectly by <u>collision theory</u>. It's simple really. The <u>rate</u> of a chemical reaction depends on:

1) The <u>collision frequency</u> of reacting particles (how <u>often</u> they collide). The <u>more</u> collisions there are the <u>faster</u> the reaction is. E.g. doubling the frequency of collisions doubles the rate.

2) The energy <u>transferred</u> during a collision. Particles have to collide with <u>enough energy</u> for the collision to be successful.

A successful collision is a collision that ends in the particles reacting to form products.

The <u>minimum</u> amount of energy that particles need to react is called the <u>activation energy</u>. Particles need this much energy to <u>break the bonds</u> in the reactants and start the reaction. The <u>greater</u> the activation energy, the <u>more</u> energy needed to <u>start</u> the reaction — this has to be <u>supplied</u>, e.g. by <u>heating</u> the reaction mixture.

Factors that <u>increase</u> the <u>number</u> of collisions (so that a <u>greater proportion</u> of reacting particles collide) or the amount of <u>energy</u> particles collide with will <u>increase</u> the <u>rate</u> of the reaction (see next page for more).

Get a fast, furious reaction — tickle your teacher...

Collision theory's essential for understanding how different factors affect the rate of reaction — so make sure you understand it before moving on to the rest of the section.

Q1   What is meant by the term activation energy?   [1 mark]

Factors Affecting the Rate of Reaction

I'd ask you to <u>guess</u> what this page is about, but the <u>title</u> pretty much says it all really. Read on...

The Rate of Reaction Depends on Four Things

1) <u>Temperature</u>.
2) The <u>concentration</u> of a solution or the <u>pressure</u> of gas.
3) <u>Surface area</u> — this changes depending on the size of the lumps of a solid.
4) The presence of a <u>catalyst</u> (see next page).

The More Collisions, the Higher the Rate of Reaction

The <u>effects</u> of temperature, concentration (or pressure) and surface area on the <u>rate of reaction</u> can be explained in terms of <u>how often</u> the reacting particles <u>collide</u> and how much <u>energy</u> they collide with...

Increasing the Temperature Increases Rate

1) When the <u>temperature is increased</u> the particles <u>move faster</u>. If they move faster, they're going to have <u>more collisions</u>.

2) Higher temperatures also increase the <u>energy</u> of the collisions, since the particles are moving <u>faster</u>. Reactions <u>only happen</u> if the particles collide with <u>enough energy</u>.

3) This means that at <u>higher</u> temperatures there will be more <u>successful collisions</u> (more particles will <u>collide</u> with <u>enough energy</u> to react). So <u>increasing</u> the temperature <u>increases</u> the rate of reaction.

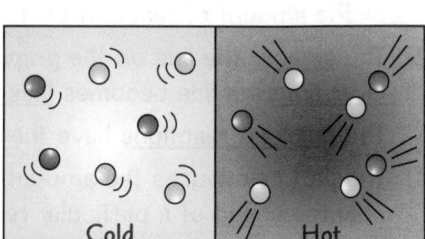

Cold   Hot

Increasing Concentration (or Pressure) Increases Rate

1) If a <u>solution</u> is made more <u>concentrated</u> it means there are more particles of <u>reactant</u> in the same volume. This makes collisions <u>more likely</u>, so the reaction rate <u>increases</u>.

2) In a <u>gas</u>, increasing the <u>pressure</u> means that the particles are <u>more crowded</u>. This means that the frequency of <u>collisions</u> between particles will <u>increase</u> — so the rate of reaction will also <u>increase</u>.

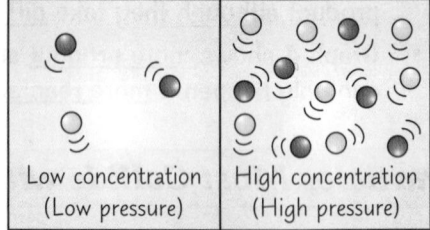

Low concentration (Low pressure)   High concentration (High pressure)

Smaller Solid Particles (or More Surface Area) Means a Higher Rate

1) If one reactant is a <u>solid</u>, breaking it into <u>smaller</u> pieces will <u>increase its surface area to volume ratio</u> (i.e. more of the solid will be exposed, compared to its overall volume).

2) The particles around it will have <u>more area to work on</u>, so the frequency of collisions will <u>increase</u>.

3) This means that the rate of reaction is faster for solids with a larger <u>surface area to volume</u> ratio.

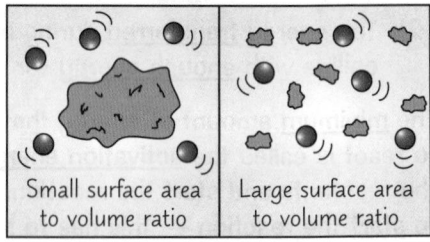

Small surface area to volume ratio   Large surface area to volume ratio

Increase your concentration — burn through that exam paper...

Remember — more collisions mean a faster reaction. But don't be fooled as not every collision results in a reaction.

Q1   Describe the two factors, in terms of collisions, that affect the rate of reaction.   [2 marks]

Q2   Why does raising the temperature increase the rate of a reaction?   [3 marks]

Catalysts

Catalysts are very important for commercial reasons — they increase reaction rate and reduce energy costs in industrial reactions. If that's not reason enough to learn this page, I don't know what is. (Oh, apart from "exams"...)

A Catalyst Increases the Rate of a Reaction

1) A catalyst is a substance which increases the rate of a reaction, without being chemically changed or used up in the reaction.

2) Using a catalyst won't change the products of the reaction — so the reaction equation will stay the same.

3) Because it isn't used up, you only need a tiny bit to catalyse large amounts of reactants.

4) Catalysts tend to be very fussy about which reactions they catalyse though — you can't just stick any old catalyst in a reaction and expect it to work.

5) Catalysts work by decreasing the activation energy (see page 59) needed for a reaction to occur.

6) They do this by providing an alternative reaction pathway that has a lower activation energy.

7) As a result, more of the particles have at least the minimum amount of energy needed for a reaction to occur when the particles collide.

You Can Show the Effect of a Catalyst using Reaction Profiles

1) The activation energy for a reaction can be shown on a reaction profile — it's the difference between the energy of the reactants and the highest point on the curve.

2) You can use reaction profiles to compare the activation energy of a reaction with and without a catalyst.

There's more on reaction profiles on p.55.

3) The highest point on the curve for a reaction with a catalyst will be lower than without a catalyst.

4) Here are reaction profiles showing how a catalyst affects the activation energy for an exothermic and endothermic reaction (see page 55 for more on exo- and endothermic reactions).

Exothermic:

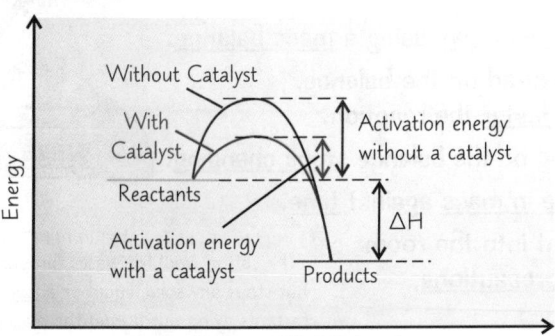

Endothermic:

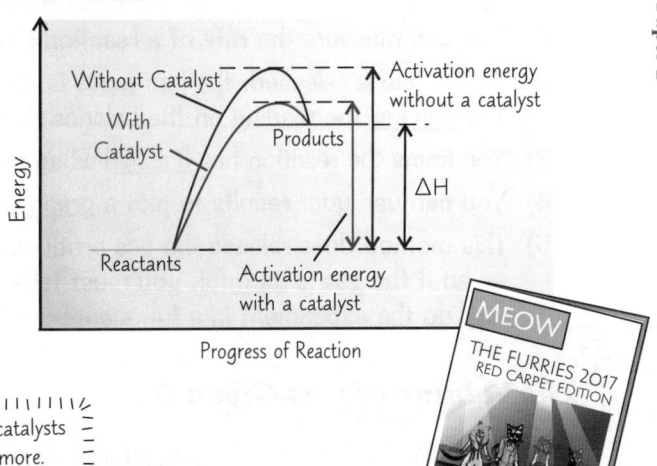

You can carry out experiments to investigate how catalysts affect the rate of a reaction — see page 64 for more.

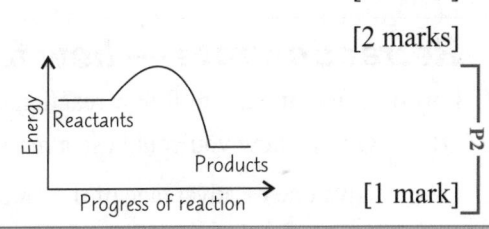

MEOW
THE FURRIES 2017
RED CARPET EDITION
HOW TO GET THAT A-LIST RED CARPET LOOK

Paper 2

I wish there was a catalyst for making my takeaway arrive...

Catalysts are really handy. Some reactions take a very long time to happen by themselves which isn't good for industrial reactions. Catalysts help to produce an acceptable amount of product in an acceptable length of time.

Q1 Give the definition of a catalyst. [2 marks]

Q2 Explain how a catalyst changes the rate of a reaction. [2 marks]

Q3 A student carries out the decomposition of hydrogen peroxide. The reaction profile for this reaction is shown on the right. Describe how the height of the curve on the reaction profile would change if the reaction was carried out in the presence of a catalyst. [1 mark]

Section 5 — Physical Chemistry

Measuring Rates of Reaction

Reactions can be <u>fast</u> or <u>slow</u> — you've probably already realised that. It's exciting stuff. Honest.

The Speed of a Reaction Can be Measured

The <u>speed of a reaction</u> can be observed <u>either</u> by how quickly the reactants are used up or how quickly the products are formed. It's usually a lot easier to measure <u>products forming</u>.

The rate of reaction can be calculated using the following equation:

$$\text{Rate of Reaction} = \frac{\text{Amount of reactant used or amount of product formed}}{\text{Time}}$$

You Can Do Experiments to Follow Reaction Rates

There are different ways that the rate of a reaction can be <u>measured</u>. Here are three examples:

Precipitation

1) This method works for any reaction where mixing <u>two see-through solutions</u> produces a <u>precipitate</u>, which <u>clouds</u> the solution.

2) You <u>mix</u> the two reactant solutions and put the flask on a piece of paper that has a <u>mark</u> on it.

3) <u>Observe</u> the mark through the mixture and measure how long it takes for the mark to be <u>obscured</u>. The <u>faster</u> it disappears, the <u>faster</u> the reaction.

4) The result is <u>subjective</u> — <u>different people</u> might not agree on <u>exactly</u> when the mark 'disappears'.

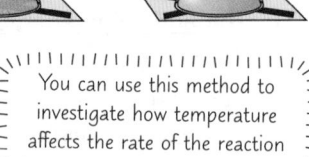

You can use this method to investigate how temperature affects the rate of the reaction between sodium thiosulfate and hydrochloric acid. See page 64.

Change in Mass (Usually Gas Given Off)

1) You can measure the rate of a reaction that <u>produces a gas</u> using a <u>mass balance</u>.

2) As the gas is released, the <u>lost mass</u> is easily measured on the balance. The <u>quicker</u> the reading on the balance <u>drops</u>, the <u>faster</u> the reaction.

3) You know the reaction has <u>finished</u> when the reading on the balance <u>stops changing</u>.

4) You can use your results to plot a <u>graph</u> of <u>change in mass</u> against <u>time</u>.

5) This method does release the gas produced straight into the room — so if the gas is <u>harmful</u>, you must take <u>safety precautions</u>, e.g. do the experiment in a <u>fume cupboard</u>.

The cotton wool lets gases through but stops any solid, liquid or aqueous reactants flying out during the reaction.

The Volume of Gas Given Off

1) This involves the use of a <u>gas syringe</u> to measure the <u>volume</u> of gas given off.

2) The <u>more</u> gas given off during a set <u>time interval</u>, the <u>faster</u> the reaction.

3) You can tell the reaction has <u>finished</u> when <u>no more gas</u> is produced.

4) You can use your results to plot a graph of <u>gas volume</u> against <u>time elapsed</u>.

5) You need to be careful that you're using the <u>right size</u> gas syringe for your experiment though — if the reaction is too <u>vigorous</u>, you can blow the plunger out of the end of the syringe.

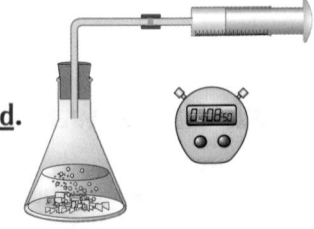

Retraction rate — how fast my mates disappear when I tell a joke...

Lots of different ways to follow reaction rates here — well... three. Precipitation, mass loss and gas formation.

Q1   Outline how you could use a mass balance to measure the rate of a reaction where a gas is formed.   [3 marks]

Q2   Give one disadvantage of the precipitation method when used to follow the rate of a reaction.   [1 mark]

Rate of Reaction Experiments [PRACTICAL]

You'll probably have to <u>measure</u> the <u>rate of a reaction</u> in class at some point. Time to learn how to do it...

You Can Measure how Surface Area Affects Rate

Here's how you can carry out an experiment to measure the effect of <u>surface area</u> on <u>rate</u>, using marble chips and hydrochloric acid.

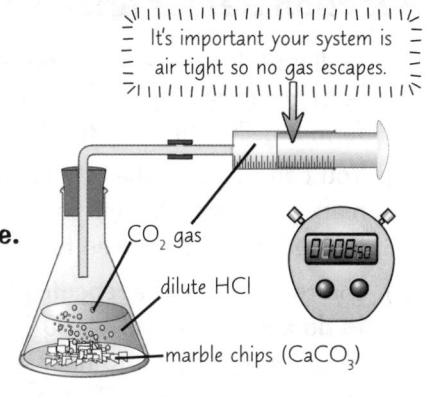

It's important your system is air tight so no gas escapes.

1) Set the apparatus up as shown in the diagram on the right.

2) Measure the <u>volume</u> of gas produced using a <u>gas syringe</u>.
Take readings at <u>regular time intervals</u> and record the results in a table.

3) You can plot a <u>graph</u> of your results —
time goes on the <u>x-axis</u> and volume goes on the <u>y-axis</u>.

4) <u>Repeat</u> the experiment with <u>exactly the same volume</u> and <u>concentration</u> of acid, and <u>exactly the same mass</u> of marble chips, but with the marble <u>more crunched up</u>.

5) Then <u>repeat</u> with the same mass of <u>powdered chalk</u>.

CO_2 gas

dilute HCl

marble chips ($CaCO_3$)

Marble and chalk are both made of calcium carbonate ($CaCO_3$).

Finer Particles of Solid Mean a Higher Rate

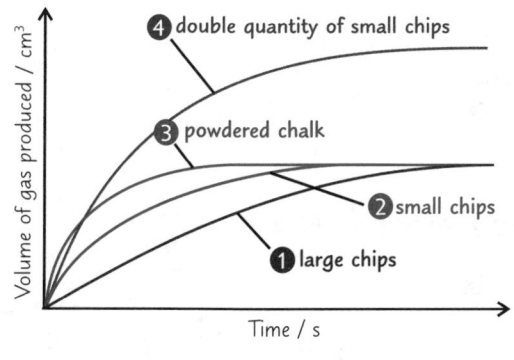

Volume of gas produced / cm^3

④ double quantity of small chips

③ powdered chalk

② small chips

① large chips

Time / s

1) Using <u>finer particles</u> means that the marble has a <u>larger surface area</u>.

2) <u>Lines 1 to 3</u> on the graph on the left show that the <u>finer</u> the particles are (and the <u>greater</u> the surface area of the solid reactants), the <u>sooner</u> the reaction finishes and so the <u>faster</u> the reaction.

3) <u>Line 4</u> shows the reaction if a <u>greater mass</u> of small marble chips is added.
The <u>extra surface area</u> gives a <u>faster reaction</u> and there is also <u>more gas evolved</u> overall.

Changing the Concentration of Acid Affects the Rate too

The reaction between marble chips and hydrochloric acid is also good for measuring how <u>changing the reactant concentration</u> affects reaction rate.

You could also measure the rate of these reactions by measuring the loss of mass as the gas is produced.

More Concentrated Solutions Mean a Higher Rate

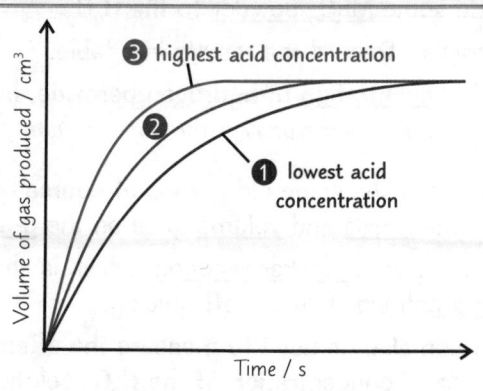

Volume of gas produced / cm^3

③ highest acid concentration

②

① lowest acid concentration

Time / s

1) You can measure the effect of <u>concentration</u> on rate by following the <u>same method</u> described above. However, this time you repeat the experiment with exactly the same mass and surface area of marble chips and exactly the same volume of acid, but using <u>different concentrations</u> of acid.

2) <u>Lines 1 to 3</u> on the graph show that a <u>higher</u> concentration gives a <u>faster reaction</u>, with the reaction <u>finishing</u> sooner.

I prefer chalk to marble chips — I like the finer things in life...

These are just two rate experiments you could carry out. There are different methods for investigating the effect of temperature and catalysts. But that's all still to come. I bet you're just itching to read on...

Q1   Describe how you could investigate how the surface area of calcium carbonate affects the rate of reaction between calcium carbonate and hydrochloric acid.   [3 marks]

More Rate of Reaction Experiments

Another page, some more <u>reaction rate</u> experiments. But one of these involves a pretty precipitation reaction...

Reaction Rate is Affected by Temperature

1) Sodium thiosulfate and hydrochloric acid are both <u>clear solutions</u>. They react together to form a <u>yellow precipitate</u> of <u>sulfur</u>.

2) You can measure the rate by watching a black mark <u>disappear</u> through the <u>cloudy sulfur</u> and <u>timing</u> how long it takes to go.

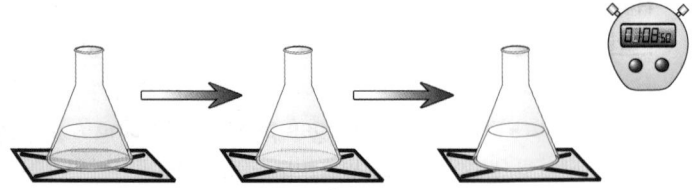

3) The reaction can be <u>repeated</u> for solutions at different <u>temperatures</u>. In practice, that's quite hard to do accurately and safely (it's not a good idea to heat an acid directly). The best way to do it is to use a <u>water bath</u> to heat both solutions to the right temperature <u>before you mix them</u>.

4) The <u>depth</u> of liquid must be kept the <u>same</u> each time, of course.

5) The results will of course show that the <u>higher</u> the temperature the <u>quicker</u> the reaction and therefore the <u>less time</u> it takes for the mark to <u>disappear</u>. These are typical results:

	Temperature (°C)	20	25	30	35	40
independent variable ⟹	Time taken for mark to disappear (s)	193	151	112	87	52

dependent variable ⟹

This reaction can <u>also</u> be used to test the effects of <u>concentration</u>.

One sad thing about this reaction is it <u>doesn't</u> give a set of graphs. Well I think it's sad. All you get is a set of <u>readings</u> of how long it took till the mark disappeared for each temperature. Boring.

Although you could draw a graph of temperature against 1/time which will give you an approximate rate.

You Can Measure How Using Catalysts Affects Rate

PRACTICAL

This is a <u>good</u> reaction for showing the effect of different <u>catalysts</u>.

The <u>decomposition</u> of hydrogen peroxide (H_2O_2) is:

$$2H_2O_{2\ (aq)} \rightarrow 2H_2O_{(l)} + O_{2\ (g)}$$

1) This is normally quite <u>slow</u> but a bit of <u>manganese(IV) oxide (MnO_2)</u> <u>catalyst</u> speeds it up no end. Other catalysts which work are copper(II) oxide (CuO) and zinc oxide (ZnO).

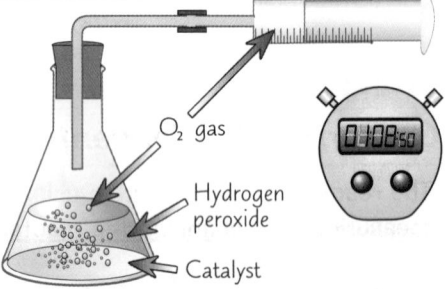

O_2 gas

Hydrogen peroxide

Catalyst

2) <u>Oxygen gas</u> is given off, which provides an <u>ideal way</u> to measure the rate of reaction using the good ol' <u>gas syringe</u> method.

- Set up the apparatus as shown in the diagram above. Add some <u>MnO_2 powder</u> to the H_2O_2.
- Measure the <u>volume</u> of gas produced at <u>regular time intervals</u>. Record the results in a table.
- Repeat the experiment with <u>exactly the same volume</u> and <u>concentration</u> of hydrogen peroxide, but using a <u>different catalyst</u>, e.g. copper oxide. The amount of catalyst must be kept the same though.

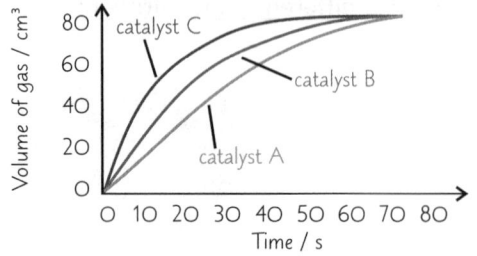

3) You can then draw the same old graphs of course — time goes on the <u>x-axis</u> and <u>volume</u> goes on the <u>y-axis</u>.

4) <u>Better</u> catalysts give a <u>quicker reaction</u>, which is shown by a <u>steeper graph</u> which levels off quickly.

5) This reaction can also be used to measure the effects of <u>temperature</u>, or of <u>concentration</u> of the H_2O_2 solution. The graphs will look just the same.

Catalyst — a list of the cows you own...

You don't need to know all the details of these specific reactions — it's the experimental methods you need to learn.

Q1   Sodium thiosulfate and hydrochloric acid react to form a precipitate.
Describe an experiment to investigate how temperature affects the rate of this reaction.   [4 marks]

Reversible Reactions

Reversible reactions — products forming from reactants and reactants forming from products. I can't keep up...

Reversible Reactions Can Go Forwards and Backwards

A <u>reversible reaction</u> is one where the <u>products</u> of the reaction can react with each other and <u>convert back</u> to the original reactants. In other words, <u>it can go both ways</u>.

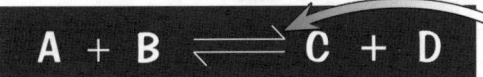

This is the symbol for a reversible reaction.

The <u>thermal decomposition of ammonium chloride</u> is a reversible reaction.

1) Ammonium chloride is a <u>white solid</u>. When it's heated it breaks down into the gases <u>ammonia</u> and <u>hydrogen chloride</u> — this is the <u>forward reaction</u>.

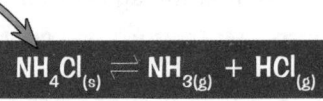

$$NH_4Cl_{(s)} \rightleftharpoons NH_{3(g)} + HCl_{(g)}$$

2) If you let it cool the <u>ammonia</u> and <u>hydrogen chloride</u> react to <u>re-form</u> the solid — this is the <u>backward reaction</u>.

The <u>dehydration of copper(II) sulfate</u> is another example of a reversible reaction (see page 53).

Reversible Reactions Will Reach Dynamic Equilibrium

1) If a reversible reaction takes place in a <u>closed system</u> then a state of <u>equilibrium</u> will always be reached.

2) <u>Equilibrium</u> means that the <u>concentrations</u> of reactants and products will reach a certain <u>balance</u> and stay there. (A '<u>closed system</u>' just means that none of the reactants or products can <u>escape</u>.)

3) It is in fact a <u>DYNAMIC EQUILIBRIUM</u>, which means that the reactions are still taking place in <u>both directions</u>, but the <u>overall effect is nil</u> because the forward and reverse reactions <u>cancel</u> each other out. The reactions are taking place at <u>exactly the same rate</u> in both directions.

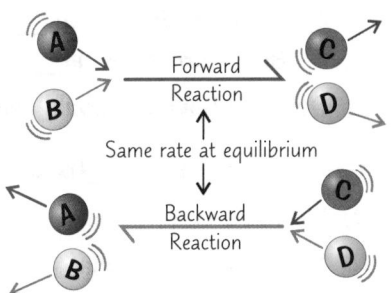

Changing Temperature and Pressure Can Get You More Product

1) In a reversible reaction the '<u>position of equilibrium</u>' (the relative amounts of reactants and products) depends <u>very strongly</u> on the <u>temperature</u> and <u>pressure</u> of the reacting mixture.

2) If you <u>deliberately alter</u> the temperature and pressure you can <u>move</u> the "position of equilibrium" to give <u>more product</u> and <u>less</u> reactants — so the position shifts to the <u>right</u>.

TEMPERATURE All reactions are <u>exothermic</u> in one direction and <u>endothermic</u> in the other (see page 55).

- If you <u>raise</u> the <u>temperature</u>, the <u>endothermic</u> reaction will increase to <u>use up</u> the extra heat.
- If you <u>reduce</u> the <u>temperature</u>, the <u>exothermic</u> reaction will increase to <u>give out</u> more heat.

PRESSURE Most gaseous reactions have <u>more moles</u> of gas on one side than on the other.

- If you <u>raise</u> the <u>pressure</u> it will encourage the reaction which produces <u>fewer moles</u> of gas.
- If you <u>lower</u> the <u>pressure</u> it will encourage the reaction which produces <u>more moles</u> of gas.

3) Adding a catalyst has <u>no effect</u> on the position of equilibrium. This is because it <u>speeds up</u> the forward reaction and the backward reaction by the <u>same amount</u>.

Paper 2

Dynamic equilibrium — lots of activity, but not to any great effect*...

Keep an eagle eye out for that arrow that shows you that a reaction is reversible. I'd hate you to miss it.

Q1 Explain what is meant by the term 'reversible reaction'. [1 mark]

Q2 What is dynamic equilibrium? [3 marks]

bit like the England football team.

Revision Questions for Section 5

We'll you've almost made it — you're just one more page away from a lovely cup of tea and a biscuit...
* Try these questions and <u>tick off each one</u> when you <u>get it right</u>.
* When you've done <u>all the questions</u> for a topic and are <u>completely happy</u> with it, tick off the topic.

<u>Energy Transfer in Reactions (p.55-56)</u> ☑

1) In an exothermic reaction is heat transferred to or from the surroundings? ☑
2) Define what is meant by an endothermic reaction. ☑
3) What is the symbol for change in enthalpy? ☑
4) Draw a reaction profile for an endothermic reaction. ☑
5) Describe how you could measure the temperature change in a neutralisation reaction. ☑
6) Why are draught excluders used in calorimetry experiments? ☑

<u>Calculating Enthalpy Changes (p.57-58)</u> ☑

7) What is the equation for calculating the heat energy transferred in a reaction? ☑
8) For the following sentences, use either 'endothermic' or 'exothermic' to fill in the blanks:
   a) Bond breaking is an _____ process.
   b) Bond forming is an _____ process. ☑
9) Describe how you could calculate the enthalpy change of a reaction using bond energies. ☑

<u>Rates of Reaction (p.59-64)</u> ☑

10) Sketch a graph to show how the amount of product formed in a reaction changes over time. ☑
11) Name four things that the rate of a reaction depends on. ☑
12) Explain how each of the four factors that affect reaction rate
increases the number of successful collisions between particles. ☑
13) What is a catalyst? ☑
14) Show the effect of a catalyst on the reaction profile of an exothermic reaction. ☑
15) Explain how you could follow the rate of a reaction where
two colourless solutions react to form a precipitate. ☑
16) Describe how you could investigate the effect of increasing HCl concentration
on the rate of reaction between HCl and marble chips. ☑
17) Describe how you could measure the rate of reaction for the decomposition of hydrogen peroxide. ☑

<u>Reversible Reactions (p.65)</u> ☑

18) What is the symbol for a reversible reaction? ☑
19) Which one of the following statements is true?
   a) In a reaction at equilibrium, there is the same amount of products as reactants.
   b) If the forward reaction in a reversible reaction is exothermic, then the reverse reaction is endothermic.
   c) If the equilibrium of a system lies towards the products, then the concentration
      of products is less than the concentration of reactants. ☑
20) How does changing the temperature and pressure of a reversible reaction alter the equilibrium position? ☑

Organic Compounds

This section's all about organic chemistry — in other words, molecules that contain carbon.

There are Loads of Ways of Representing Organic Compounds

Type of formula	What it shows you	Formula for Ethene
General formula	An algebraic formula that can describe any member of a family of compounds.	C_nH_{2n} (for all alkenes)
Empirical formula	The simplest whole number ratio of atoms of each element in a compound (cancel the numbers down if possible).	CH_2
Molecular formula	The actual number of atoms of each element in a molecule.	C_2H_4
Displayed formula	Shows how all the atoms are arranged, and all the bonds between them.	$\underset{H}{\overset{H}{\diagdown}}C=C\underset{H}{\overset{H}{\diagup}}$
Structural formula	Shows the arrangement of atoms carbon by carbon, with the attached hydrogens and functional groups (see below).	CH_2CH_2

Compounds in a Homologous Series Share Similar Chemical Properties

1) A homologous series is a group of compounds that can all be represented by the same general formula.

2) You can use a general formula to work out the molecular formula of any member of a homologous series.

> E.g. Alkanes are a homologous series that only contain carbon and hydrogen atoms — there's more about them on page 73.
> The general formula for alkanes is C_nH_{2n+2}. So the first alkane in the series is $C_1H_{(2\times1)+2} = CH_4$, the second is $C_2H_{(2\times2)+2} = C_2H_6$, etc.

3) Molecules in a homologous series contain the same functional group.

4) A functional group is a group of atoms that determine how a compound typically reacts.

5) This means that compounds in a homologous series often react in similar ways.

6) These are the functional groups you need to know:

Alkenes

Functional Group: $\underset{H}{\overset{R}{\diagdown}}C=C\underset{R}{\overset{H}{\diagup}}$

There's more on alkenes on p.74

R is used in place of a carbon chain that is attached to the functional group.

Alcohols

Functional Group: $R-O-H$

There's more on alcohols on p.75

Carboxylic Acids:

Functional Group: $R-\overset{\overset{\displaystyle O}{\|}}{C}-OH$

There's more on carboxylic acids on p.77

Esters

Functional Group: $R-\overset{\overset{\displaystyle O}{\|}}{C}-O-R$

There's more on esters on p.78

Paper 2

Our drummer broke his sticks — but we're a functional group again...

The main things to take away from this page are that members of homologous series share the same functional groups and a functional group is a particular group of atoms. You'll meet some homologous series in more detail later on...

Q1   Give the definition of a functional group.   [1 mark]

Naming Organic Compounds

<u>Organic compounds</u> used to be given whatever names people fancied, but these names led to <u>confusion</u> between different countries. Luckily, chemists got together and came up with a system...

Nomenclature is a Fancy Word for the Naming of Organic Compounds

The <u>IUPAC</u> system for naming <u>organic compounds</u> was invented as an international language for chemistry. It can be used to give any organic compound a name using these rules of nomenclature...

1) Count the carbon atoms in the <u>carbon chain</u> — this gives you the stem.

No. of Carbons	1	2	3	4	5	6
Stem	meth-	eth-	prop-	but-	pent-	hex-

2) The <u>main functional group</u> of the molecule usually tells you what <u>homologous series</u> the molecule is in (see previous page), and so gives you the <u>prefix</u> or <u>suffix</u> — see the table below.

Homologous Series	Prefix or Suffix	Example
alkanes	–ane	propane — $CH_3CH_2CH_3$
alkenes	–ene	but-2-ene — $CH_3CHCHCH_3$
alcohols	–ol	ethanol — CH_3CH_2OH
carboxylic acids	–oic acid	ethanoic acid — CH_3COOH
esters	Prefix: alkyl– (–yl) Suffix: –anoate	ethyl ethanoate — $CH_3C(=O)OCH_2CH_3$

Paper 2

Paper 2

3) Number the carbon chain so that the functional group has the lowest possible number.

4) If there's more than one <u>identical</u> functional group, use <u>di-</u> (2), <u>tri-</u> (3) or <u>tetra-</u> (4) before the suffix.

<u>Example 1:</u> $CH_2CHCH_2CH_3$

1) The carbon chain is <u>4</u> carbons long. So the stem is '<u>but–</u>'.

2) The main functional group is a carbon-carbon double bond. So it is an alkene and the name will end in '<u>–ene</u>'.

3) Numbering the carbon chain so that one of the carbons in the C=C group has the lowest possible number puts the C=C group on <u>carbon 1</u>.

4) This means that the systematic name for the molecule is: <u>but-1-ene</u>.

I will name this species the duck-beaver-otter...

Paper 2

<u>Example 2:</u> $CH_3CH_2CH_2OH$

1) The carbon chain is <u>3</u> carbons long. So the stem is '<u>prop–</u>'.

2) The main functional group is <u>-OH</u>, so the suffix is <u>-ol</u>.

3) Numbering the carbon chain puts the OH on <u>carbon 1</u>.

4) This means that the systematic name for the molecule is: <u>propan-1-ol</u>.
This molecule can sometimes be called just <u>propanol</u>.

If this molecule had 2 -OH groups it would be called propan<u>diol</u> — see page 80.

A rose by any other systematic name would smell as sweet...

In chemistry, the rules for naming can seem complicated but if you look at it logically and take your time you'll get it spot on. Why not have a go at the question below just to make sure? Then, do some yoga to relax.

Q1   Name this alkene:

H   H
| |
H–C–C=C–C–H
| | | |
H H H H

[1 mark]

Isomers

Isomerism is great fun. It's all about how many ways there are of making <u>different molecules</u> from the <u>same molecular formula</u>. They can be a bit sneaky, though, so best be on your guard...

Isomers Have the Same Molecular Formula

1) Two molecules are isomers of one another if they have the <u>same molecular formula</u> but the atoms are <u>arranged differently</u>.

2) This means their <u>structural formulae</u> are different.

3) Isomers can be hard to spot — here are some things you need to look out for:

Differently Shaped Carbon Chains

1) The <u>carbons</u> could be arranged differently — for example, as a <u>straight chain</u>, or <u>branched</u> (one of the carbons being bonded to more than two other carbons) in different ways.

2) These isomers have <u>similar chemical properties</u> (they will react in similar ways) — but their <u>physical properties</u>, like boiling point, will be <u>different</u> because of the change in shape of the molecule.

> E.g. <u>both</u> of these molecules have the formula C_4H_{10}:
>
> Butane   Methylpropane

Functional Groups in Different Places

1) The <u>arrangement</u> of carbon atoms could be the same, and the isomers could have the same <u>functional group</u>, but the functional group could be attached to a <u>different carbon atom</u>.

2) These isomers also have <u>different physical properties</u>.

> E.g. <u>both</u> of these molecules have the formula C_4H_8:
>
> But-1-ene   But-2-ene

Different Functional Groups

1) The same atoms could be arranged into <u>different functional groups</u>.

2) These isomers have very <u>different physical</u> and <u>chemical</u> properties.

> E.g. <u>both</u> of these molecules have the formula $C_4H_8O_2$:
>
> Methyl propanoate   Butanoic acid

Isomermaids — the chemists of the seas...

This page has a lot of information so make sure you go over it a few times so you understand it fully.

Q1   What is meant by the term isomer?   [1 mark]

Crude Oil

Over millions of years, high temperatures and pressures cause the buried remains of plants and animals to turn into crude oil. Then we come along and drill it up.

Crude Oil is Separated into Different Hydrocarbon Fractions

Crude oil is a mixture of substances, most of which are hydrocarbons — molecules which are made of only carbon and hydrogen. The different compounds in crude oil are separated by fractional distillation:

1) The oil is heated until most of it has turned into gas. The gases enter a fractionating column (and the liquid bit, bitumen, is drained off at the bottom).

2) In the column there's a temperature gradient (i.e. it's hot at the bottom and gets gradually cooler as you go up). When the substances that make up crude oil reach a part of the column where the temperature is lower than their boiling point they condense (turn back into a liquid).

3) The longer hydrocarbons have high boiling points. They condense and drain out of the column early on, when they're near the bottom.

4) The shorter hydrocarbons have lower boiling points. They turn to liquid and drain out much later on, near to the top of the column where it's cooler.

5) Bubble caps in the fractionating column stop the separated liquids from running back down the column and remixing. You end up with the crude oil mixture separated out into different fractions. Each fraction contains a mixture of hydrocarbons with similar boiling points. Each fraction may contain saturated or unsaturated hydrocarbons. Saturated hydrocarbons only contain single bonds between carbon atoms whereas unsaturated hydrocarbons have double or triple bonds between carbon atoms.

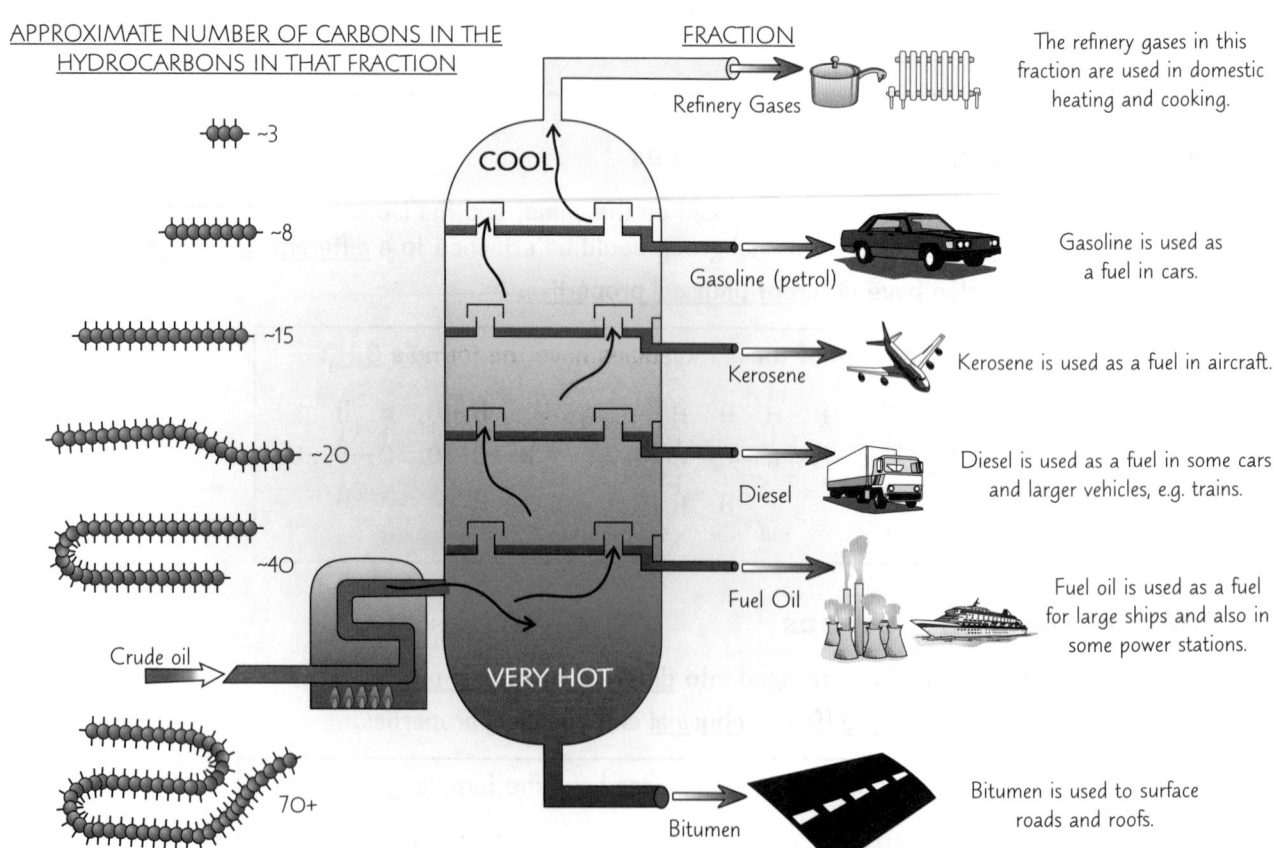

APPROXIMATE NUMBER OF CARBONS IN THE HYDROCARBONS IN THAT FRACTION

FRACTION

~3

COOL

~8

~15

~20

~40

Crude oil

VERY HOT

70+

Refinery Gases — The refinery gases in this fraction are used in domestic heating and cooking.

Gasoline (petrol) — Gasoline is used as a fuel in cars.

Kerosene — Kerosene is used as a fuel in aircraft.

Diesel — Diesel is used as a fuel in some cars and larger vehicles, e.g. trains.

Fuel Oil — Fuel oil is used as a fuel for large ships and also in some power stations.

Bitumen — Bitumen is used to surface roads and roofs.

How much petrol is there in crude oil? Just a fraction...

Crude oil is pretty useful, so it's worth having a good read of this page to make sure you know all about it.

Q1   What are hydrocarbons?   [1 mark]

Q2   Explain how crude oil is separated into fractions during fractional distillation.   [5 marks]

Cracking

The really long hydrocarbons aren't all that useful — but it's OK 'cause they can be made smaller by <u>cracking</u>.

Cracking — Splitting Up Long-Chain Hydrocarbons

1) <u>Long</u> hydrocarbons have <u>high</u> boiling points and are <u>viscous</u> (thick and gloopy).

2) <u>Shorter</u> hydrocarbons have <u>lower</u> boiling points and are much <u>thinner</u> and <u>paler</u> in colour.

3) Demand for <u>short-chain</u> hydrocarbons like octane, which is used in petrol (gasoline), is much <u>higher</u> than for longer-chain hydrocarbons.

4) So, to <u>meet</u> this demand, long-chain hydrocarbons are <u>split</u> into <u>more useful</u> short-chain molecules using <u>cracking</u>.

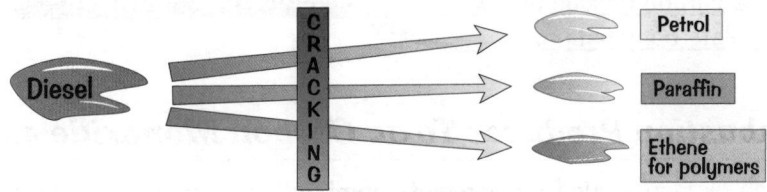

5) <u>Cracking</u> is a form of <u>thermal decomposition</u>, which just means <u>breaking</u> molecules down into <u>simpler</u> molecules by <u>heating</u> them.

6) Cracking also produces <u>alkenes</u>, which are used to make <u>polymers</u> (see page 79).

Conditions for Cracking: Heat, Plus a Catalyst

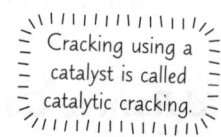

Cracking using a catalyst is called catalytic cracking.

In industry, <u>vaporised hydrocarbons</u> are passed over a <u>powdered catalyst</u> at about <u>600 °C – 700 °C</u>. <u>Silica</u> (SiO_2) or <u>alumina</u> (Al_2O_3) are used as the <u>catalyst</u>. You can carry out the reaction in the lab using simple equipment. Like this...

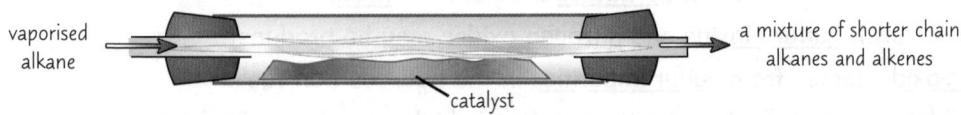

vaporised alkane

catalyst

a mixture of shorter chain alkanes and alkenes

During this reaction, the alkane is heated until it is <u>vaporised</u>. It then breaks down when it comes into contact with the catalyst, producing a mixture of <u>short-chain alkanes</u> and <u>alkenes</u>.

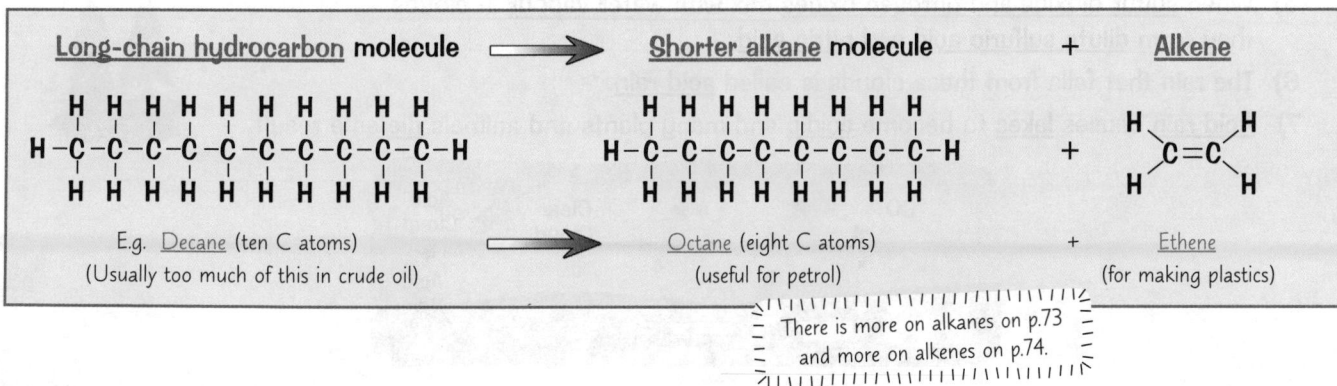

Long-chain hydrocarbon molecule	Shorter alkane molecule	+	Alkene

E.g. <u>Decane</u> (ten C atoms) → <u>Octane</u> (eight C atoms) + <u>Ethene</u>
(Usually too much of this in crude oil)   (useful for petrol)   (for making plastics)

There is more on alkanes on p.73 and more on alkenes on p.74.

Alumina's hilarious, it's always cracking the hydrocarbons up...

In that case, I better crack open another packet of biscuits so that the supply matches my stomach's large demand...

Q1   State the temperature range that cracking is normally carried out at.   [1 mark]

Q2   What two types of molecules are produced from cracking?   [2 marks]

Burning Hydrocarbons

The great thing about <u>oil</u> is the amount of energy that gets released when it's burnt. However, this does come with some downsides. For example, some of the by-products of <u>combustion</u> contribute to <u>pollution</u>.

Fuels Release Energy in Combustion Reactions

1) When you <u>burn</u> a <u>fuel</u>, it releases <u>energy</u> in the form of <u>heat</u>.

2) Burning is also known as a <u>combustion reaction</u> (see page 28) — the substance being burned reacts with <u>oxygen</u>.

3) <u>Hydrocarbons</u> make great fuels because the <u>combustion reactions</u> that happen when you burn them in <u>oxygen</u> give out <u>lots of energy</u> — the reactions are very <u>exothermic</u> (see page 55).

4) When you burn hydrocarbons in plenty of oxygen, the only products are <u>carbon dioxide</u> and <u>water</u> — this is called <u>complete combustion</u>.

> hydrocarbon + oxygen → carbon dioxide + water

Incomplete Combustion Produces Toxic Carbon Monoxide and Soot

1) If there's <u>not enough oxygen</u> around for complete combustion, you get <u>incomplete combustion</u>. This can happen in some appliances, e.g. boilers, that use carbon compounds as fuels.

2) The products of incomplete combustion contain <u>less oxygen</u> than carbon dioxide.

3) As well as carbon dioxide and water, incomplete combustion produces <u>carbon monoxide</u> (CO), a <u>toxic gas</u>, and <u>carbon</u> in the form of soot.

> In reality, incomplete combustion reactions will usually produce a mixture of H_2O, CO_2, CO and C.

- <u>Carbon monoxide</u> can combine with red blood cells and stop your blood from doing its proper job of <u>carrying oxygen</u> around the body.

- A lack of oxygen in the blood supply to the brain can lead to <u>fainting</u>, a <u>coma</u> or even <u>death</u>.

Acid Rain is Caused by Sulfur Dioxide and Nitrogen Oxides

1) A lot of the fractions obtained from <u>crude oil</u> are burnt as <u>fuels</u>.

2) When they're burnt, <u>sulfur dioxide</u> and <u>nitrogen oxides</u> may be produced.

3) The <u>sulfur dioxide</u> comes from <u>sulfur impurities</u> in the hydrocarbon fuels.

4) <u>Nitrogen oxides</u> are created when the temperature is <u>high</u> enough for the nitrogen and oxygen <u>in the air</u> to react. This often happens in car engines. Nitrogen oxides include <u>nitrogen monoxide</u> (NO) and <u>nitrogen dioxide</u> (NO_2).

5) When <u>sulfur dioxide and nitrogen oxides</u> mix with <u>water vapour</u> in clouds they form <u>dilute sulfuric acid</u> and <u>nitric acid</u>.

6) The rain that falls from these clouds is called <u>acid rain</u>.

7) <u>Acid rain</u> causes <u>lakes</u> to become <u>acidic</u> and many plants and animals <u>die</u> as a result.

Do you want to hear a joke about nitrogen monoxide? NO?

Why must there always be problems? Why can't every fuel be clean to burn and the combustion of hydrocarbons produce no pollutants? Why can't unicorns be real? Oh cruel world...

Q1   Name two possible products of the incomplete combustion of hydrocarbons that aren't produced during complete combustion.

[2 marks]

Alkanes

We're now going to look at the different types of hydrocarbons you can get. First up is the <u>alkanes</u>...

Alkanes are Saturated Hydrocarbons

1) Alkanes are hydrocarbons — they're <u>chains of carbon atoms</u> surrounded by <u>hydrogen atoms</u>.
2) Different alkanes have chains of different <u>lengths</u>.
3) Alkanes have the <u>general formula</u> C_nH_{2n+2}.

$$\text{Alkanes} = C_nH_{2n+2}$$

4) You need to know the <u>names</u> and the <u>structures</u> of the first five alkanes.

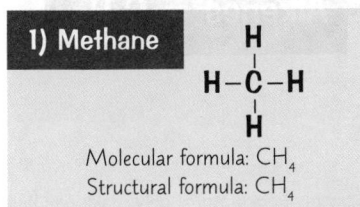

1) Methane

Molecular formula: CH_4
Structural formula: CH_4

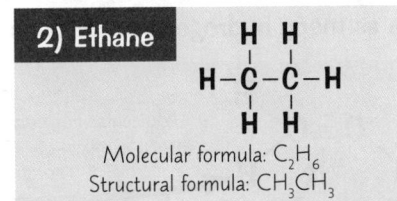

2) Ethane

Molecular formula: C_2H_6
Structural formula: CH_3CH_3

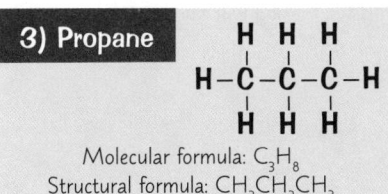

3) Propane

Molecular formula: C_3H_8
Structural formula: $CH_3CH_2CH_3$

4) Butane

Molecular formula: C_4H_{10}
Structural formula: $CH_3CH_2CH_2CH_3$

5) Pentane

Molecular formula: C_5H_{12}
Structural formula: $CH_3CH_2CH_2CH_2CH_3$

5) The diagrams above show that all the atoms have formed bonds with as many other atoms as they can. There are only <u>single bonds</u> between the <u>carbon</u> atoms — this means the molecules are <u>saturated</u>.

To help remember the names of the first four alkanes just remember: Mice Eat Peanut Butter. Pentane is five, just like a pentagon, so you'll have to remember that one on its own.

Alkanes Burn in Combustion Reactions

<u>Alkanes</u> make up the majority of hydrocarbons in crude oil and tend to combust completely in a <u>good supply of oxygen</u>.

Example: propane + oxygen → carbon dioxide + water
C_3H_8 + $5O_2$ → $3CO_2$ + $4H_2O$

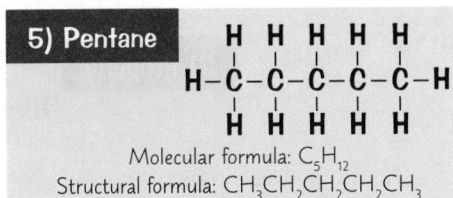

Alkane, Al saw, Al conquered.

Give it a rest, Alan!

Halogens React with Alkanes to make Haloalkanes

1) <u>Chlorine</u> and <u>bromine</u> react with alkanes in the presence of <u>ultraviolet light</u>.

2) In these reactions a <u>hydrogen</u> atom from the alkane is <u>substituted</u> with (replaced by) <u>chlorine</u> or <u>bromine</u>. So this is called a <u>substitution reaction</u>.

3) This is how bromine and methane react together to form <u>bromomethane</u>.

methane + bromine → bromomethane + hydrogen bromide

The UV here shows that the reaction needs ultraviolet light.

My brain during exam revision is a bit like alkanes — saturated...

I guess you're after a useful tip? OK here goes: Make sure you learn the general formula of alkanes and how to draw the first five alkanes. It could be super helpful in your exam, hint hint...

Q1   Ethane can react with chlorine in a substitution reaction. One of the products is hydrogen chloride. Draw the displayed formula of the other product of this reaction.

[1 mark]

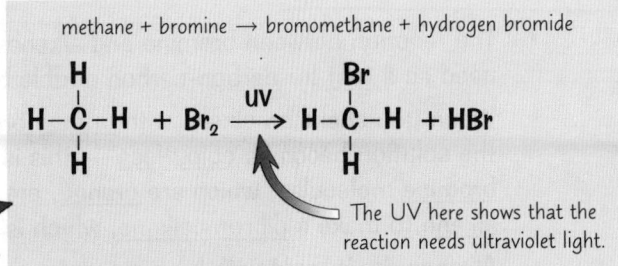

Alkenes

Alkenes are another type of hydrocarbon. They are different to alkanes because they contain a double bond.

Alkenes Have a C=C Double Bond

1) Alkenes are hydrocarbons which have a double bond between two of the carbon atoms in their chain.

2) They are unsaturated molecules because they can make more bonds — the double bond can open up, allowing the two carbon atoms to bond with other atoms (see below).

3) The first three alkenes are ethene (with two carbon atoms), propene (three Cs) and butene (four Cs).

4) All alkenes have the general formula: C_nH_{2n} — they have twice as many hydrogens as carbons.

Alkenes = C_nH_{2n}

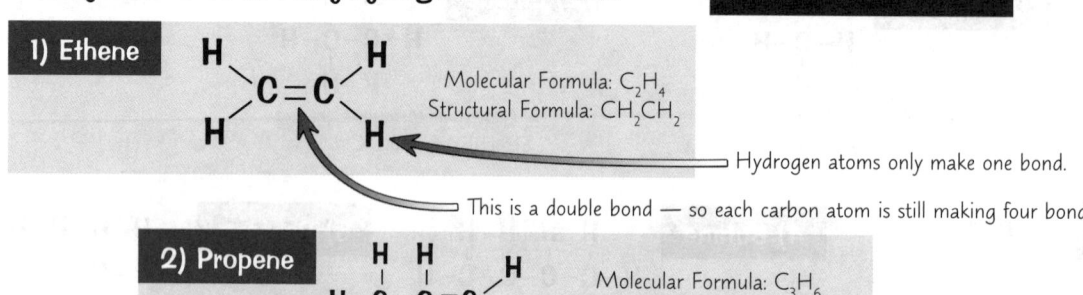

1) Ethene

Molecular Formula: C_2H_4
Structural Formula: CH_2CH_2

Hydrogen atoms only make one bond.

This is a double bond — so each carbon atom is still making four bonds.

2) Propene

Molecular Formula: C_3H_6
Structural Formula: CH_3CHCH_2

3) Butene

There are two different structures for butene — these are isomers (see page 69).

But-1-ene

Molecular Formula: C_4H_8
Structural Formula: $CH_2CHCH_2CH_3$

or

But-2-ene

Molecular Formula: C_4H_8
Structural Formula: $CH_3CHCHCH_3$

Halogens React with Alkenes, Forming Haloalkanes

There are two bromine atoms so it's called dibromoethane.

1) Halogens can react with alkenes to make haloalkanes.

2) For example bromine and ethene react together to form dibromoethane.

3) These are called addition reactions because the C=C double bond is split and a halogen atom is added to each of the carbons.

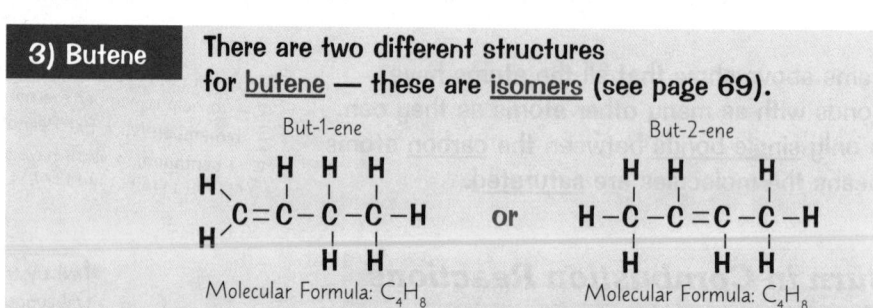

ethene + bromine → dibromoethane

- The reaction between bromine and alkenes is often used as a test for carbon-carbon double bonds.

- When you shake an alkene with orange bromine water, the solution becomes colourless — this is because the bromine molecules, which are orange, are reacting with the alkene to make a dibromoalkane, which is colourless.

- Alkanes don't react with bromine water as they don't have a double bond. So if you add an alkane to bromine water, the solution will stay orange.

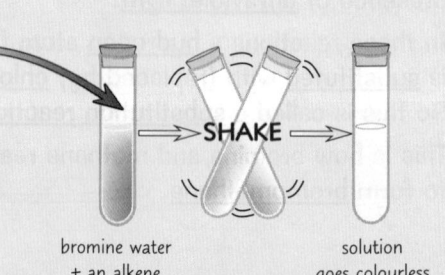

bromine water + an alkene

solution goes colourless

Hallo alkane — a nice way to greet dibromoethane...

Alkanes and alkenes look super similar but that double bond makes a lot of difference — so don't confuse them.

Q1 An alkene has 10 carbon atoms. What is the alkene's molecular formula? [1 mark]

Alcohols

This page is about different types of <u>alcohol</u> — and that's not just beer, wine and other pub favourites...

Alcohols Have an '-OH' Functional Group

1) The <u>general formula</u> of an alcohol is $C_nH_{2n+1}OH$. So an alcohol with 2 carbons has the formula C_2H_5OH.

2) All alcohols contain an <u>-OH functional group</u>. Here are the <u>first four</u> alcohols in the homologous series:

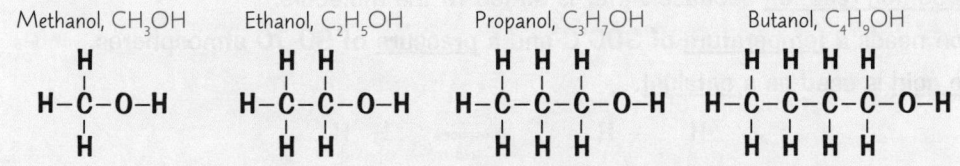

3) Don't write CH_4O instead of CH_3OH — it doesn't show the <u>-OH functional group</u>.

4) It is possible to get alcohols where the -OH group is attached to <u>different carbon atoms</u> in the carbon chain, or alcohols with <u>more than one</u> -OH group (like the ones that form condensation polymers on page 80).

Alcohols Can Be Oxidised to Form Carboxylic Acids

Oxidation can also describe the loss of electrons (see page 37).

1) When something's <u>oxidised</u>, it gains oxygen.

2) Alcohols can be oxidised to form <u>carboxylic acids</u> (see page 77). You need an oxidising agent for this, such as <u>potassium dichromate(VI) in dilute sulfuric acid</u>.

3) You need to know what happens when ethanol is <u>heated</u> with acidified potassium dichromate(VI):

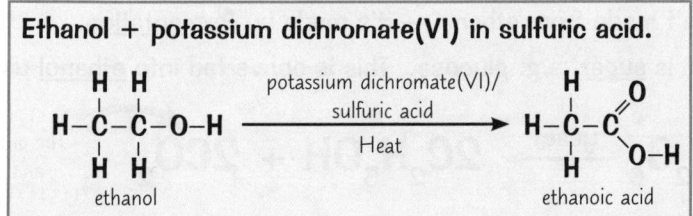

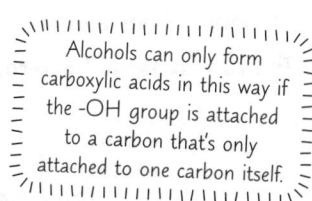

Alcohols can only form carboxylic acids in this way if the -OH group is attached to a carbon that's only attached to one carbon itself.

Microbial Oxidation Also Forms Carboxylic Acids from Alcohols

1) Some microorganisms are able to use <u>alcohols</u> as an <u>energy source</u>. To do this, they use <u>oxygen in the air</u> to oxidise alcohols.

2) <u>Carboxylic acids</u> are made as a by-product.

3) For example, the oxidation of <u>ethanol</u> produces <u>ethanoic acid</u>.

Alcohols are Oxidised when they are Burnt

1) When alcohols are burnt in enough <u>oxygen</u> (or air), they undergo <u>complete combustion</u> (see page 72).

2) The products of this reaction are <u>water</u> and <u>carbon dioxide</u>.

3) The alcohol is <u>oxidised</u> in this reaction.

Example:	ethanol	+	oxygen	→	carbon dioxide	+	water
	C_2H_5OH	+	$3O_2$	→	$2CO_2$	+	$3H_2O$

Paper 2

At every firework display, there's an -OH group and an -AH group...

Ahh alcohols, such a useful set of compounds. Make sure you learn the different ways that ethanol can be oxidised.

Q1   An alcohol has the formula CH_3OH. What is the name of this alcohol?   [1 mark]

Q2   Ethanol can be oxidised to form ethanoic acid using an oxidising agent and heat.
Name an oxidising agent that could be used in this process.   [1 mark]

P2

Production of Ethanol

The best way to make ethanol often depends on which resource is most easily available — oil or sugar.

Ethanol Can Be Produced from Ethene and Steam

1) Ethene is produced from crude oil (by cracking — see page 71).
2) Ethene (C_2H_4) will react with steam (H_2O) to make ethanol.
3) This is an addition reaction because water is added to the molecule.
4) The reaction needs a temperature of 300°C and a pressure of 60-70 atmospheres.
5) Phosphoric acid is used as a catalyst.

$$C_2H_4 + H_2O \rightarrow C_2H_5OH$$

6) At the moment this is a cheap process, because ethene's fairly cheap and not much of it is wasted.
7) The trouble is that crude oil is a non-renewable resource, which will start running out fairly soon. This means that using ethene to make ethanol will become very expensive.

Ethanol Can Also Be Produced by Fermentation

The alcohol in beer and wine, etc. isn't made from ethene — it's made by fermentation.

1) The raw material for fermentation is sugar, e.g. glucose. This is converted into ethanol using yeast.

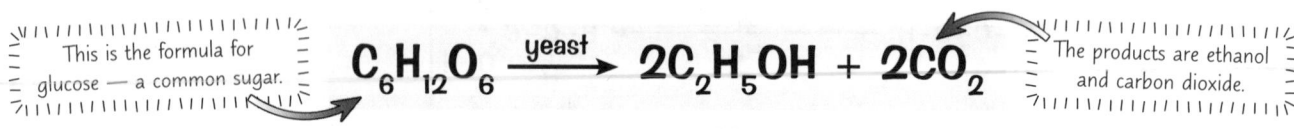

This is the formula for glucose — a common sugar.

$$C_6H_{12}O_6 \xrightarrow{\text{yeast}} 2C_2H_5OH + 2CO_2$$

The products are ethanol and carbon dioxide.

2) Yeast cells contain an enzyme. Enzymes are naturally occurring catalysts (see page 61) — they speed up reactions.
3) The fermentation mixture needs to be about 30 °C — fermentation happens fastest at this temperature. At lower temperatures, the reaction slows down. If it's too hot the enzyme in the yeast denatures (is destroyed) and the reaction would stop.
4) It's important to keep the mixture in anaerobic conditions (no oxygen). Oxygen converts the ethanol to ethanoic acid (which is what you get in vinegar — it doesn't exactly enhance the drinking experience).
5) An advantage of this process compared to the reaction of ethene with steam is that the raw materials are all renewable resources. Sugar (sugar cane) is grown as a major crop in several parts of the world, including many poorer countries. Yeast is also easy to grow.
6) There are some disadvantages to fermentation though. The ethanol you get from this process isn't very concentrated, so it needs to be distilled to increase its strength (as in whisky distilleries). It also needs to be purified.

Fancy a drink?

Fermented sugar? Alright!

Keep your spirits up, don't wine, beer positive...

I quite like this page. Well, maybe not the whole page. I just like the fact that I'm at the end of the page actually...

Q1   Name the type of molecule which is converted to ethanol by fermentation.   [1 mark]

Q2   Why is yeast required in the fermentation of glucose to produce ethanol?   [1 mark]

Q3   State the pressure required for the reaction of ethene with steam to produce ethanol.   [1 mark]

Carboxylic Acids

So you would have seen carboxylic acids mentioned on page 75. Now it's time to dive deeper into their exciting and wondrous world... (Disclaimer: may not be exciting or wondrous.)

Carboxylic Acids Have the Functional Group -COOH

1) Carboxylic acids are a homologous series of compounds that all have '-COOH' as a functional group.

2) Make sure you know the names and the structures of the first four carboxylic acids.

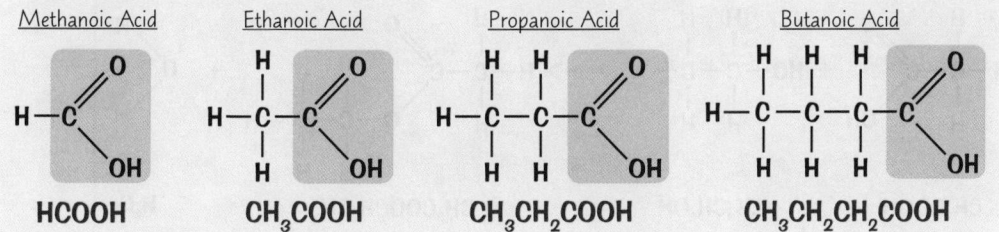

| Methanoic Acid | Ethanoic Acid | Propanoic Acid | Butanoic Acid |
| HCOOH | CH_3COOH | CH_3CH_2COOH | $CH_3CH_2CH_2COOH$ |

Carboxylic Acids React Like Other Acids

1) Carboxylic acids can react to form salts (like any other acid). The salts formed end in -anoate — e.g. methanoic acid will form a methanoate, ethanoic acid an ethanoate, etc.

2) Carboxylic acids in aqueous solution react with metal carbonates to form a salt, water and carbon dioxide. For example:

Aqueous means that a substance is dissolved in water.

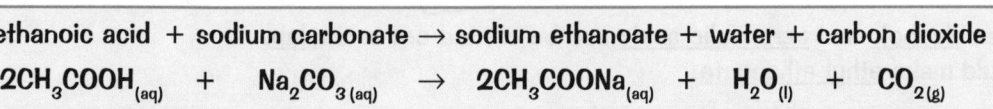

ethanoic acid + sodium carbonate → sodium ethanoate + water + carbon dioxide

$$2CH_3COOH_{(aq)} + Na_2CO_{3(aq)} \rightarrow 2CH_3COONa_{(aq)} + H_2O_{(l)} + CO_{2(g)}$$

3) Aqueous carboxylic acids react with metals to produce a salt and hydrogen. For example:

ethanoic acid + magnesium → magnesium ethanoate + hydrogen

$$2CH_3COOH_{(aq)} + 2Mg_{(s)} \rightarrow 2CH_3COOMg_{(aq)} + H_{2(g)}$$

4) Carboxylic acids are also used in the preparation of esters. Carboxylic acids react with alcohols in the presence of an acid catalyst to form esters — there's more on this on the next page.

Vinegar Contains a Carboxylic Acid

1) Ethanoic acid can be made by oxidising ethanol. Microbes, like yeast, cause the ethanol to ferment. Ethanol can also be oxidised using oxidising agents. (See p.75 for more.)

ethanol + oxygen → ethanoic acid + water

$$CH_3CH_2OH + O_2 \rightarrow CH_3COOH + H_2O$$

If you leave wine open, the ethanol in it is oxidised — this is why it goes off.

2) Ethanoic acid can then be dissolved in water to make vinegar, which is used for flavouring and preserving foods.

Ethanoic acid — it's not just for putting on your chips...

So carboxylic acids react in the same way as normal acids but you can also use them to make esters — see next page.

Q1 Which carboxylic acid is found in vinegar? [1 mark]

Q2 Sodium carbonate is added to an aqueous solution of methanoic acid.
a) Name the gas give off during the reaction. [1 mark]
b) Give the word equation for this reaction. [1 mark]

Paper 2

P2

Esters

Mix an alcohol from p.75 and a carboxylic acid from p.77, and what have you got... an <u>ester</u>, that's what.

Esters Have the Functional Group -COO-

1) <u>Esters</u> are formed from an <u>alcohol</u> and a <u>carboxylic acid</u>. ⟶ | alcohol + carboxylic acid → ester + water |

2) An <u>acid catalyst</u> is usually used (e.g. concentrated <u>sulfuric acid</u>).

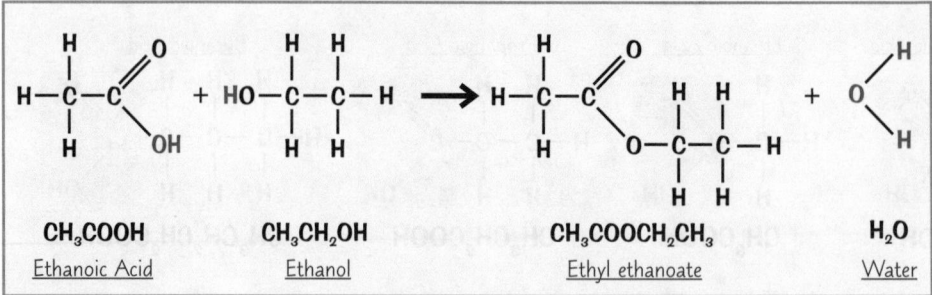

| CH₃COOH | CH₃CH₂OH | CH₃COOCH₂CH₃ | H₂O |
| Ethanoic Acid | Ethanol | Ethyl ethanoate | Water |

Their names end in '-<u>oate</u>'.
The <u>alcohol</u> forms the <u>first</u> part of the ester's name, and the <u>acid</u> forms the <u>second</u> part. ⟶

| ethanol + ethanoic acid → ethyl ethanoate + water |
| methanol + propanoic acid → methyl propanoate + water |

You Can Make Esters in the Lab   PRACTICAL

The reaction between <u>alcohols</u> and <u>carboxylic acids</u> can be carried out in the <u>lab</u>.
Here's how you would make <u>ethyl ethanoate</u>:

1) First, add a few drops of <u>concentrated sulfuric acid</u> to a boiling tube using a <u>dropping pipette</u>.

2) Add about 10 drops of <u>ethanoic acid</u>.

3) Then add an equal volume of <u>ethanol</u>.

4) Place the boiling tube in a beaker of water and place on a tripod.

5) Heat using a <u>Bunsen burner</u> until the water starts to boil, and then turn off the Bunsen.

6) After <u>1 minute</u>, remove the <u>tube</u> and allow it to <u>cool</u>.

7) Once it's cool, pour the mixture into a test tube of <u>sodium carbonate</u> solution and mix.
A <u>layer of the ester</u> should form on top of the solution.

Mixture containing sulfuric acid, ethanoic acid and ethanol.

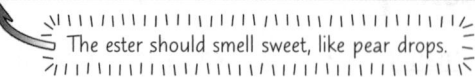
The ester should smell sweet, like pear drops.

Esters Smell Nice

1) Many esters have <u>pleasant smells</u> — often quite <u>sweet and fruity</u>.
They're also <u>volatile</u>, which means they <u>evaporate</u> (turn into gases) easily.

2) Because of these properties, esters are used in <u>perfumes</u>
(the evaporated molecules can be detected by smell receptors in your nose).

3) Esters are also used to make <u>food flavourings</u> — e.g. there are esters
that smell or taste of rum, apple, orange, banana, grape, pineapple, etc.

What's a chemist's favourite chocolate? Ester eggs...

Who'd have thought those pear drops your gran's such a fan of contained esters instead of pears?
It's a crazy old world. Make sure you're clued up on esters before you turn the page.

Q1   Draw the structural formula of the ester made by reacting ethanoic acid with methanol.   [1 mark]

Addition Polymers

Polymers are made by joining lots of little molecules together in long chains. Magic.

Addition Polymers are Made From Unsaturated Monomers

1) Polymers are substances of high average relative molecular mass made by joining up lots of small repeating units called monomers. The monomers that make up addition polymers have a double covalent bond.

2) Lots of unsaturated monomer molecules (alkenes — see p.74) can open up their carbon-carbon double bonds and join together to form polymer chains. This is called addition polymerisation.

Ethene (C_2H_4) becoming poly(ethene) — $(C_2H_4)_n$:

many single ethenes → pressure and catalyst → poly(ethene)

The 'n' represents 'any number' — it just means you start with lots of ethene molecules.

Propene (C_3H_6) becoming poly(propene) — $(C_3H_6)_n$:

many single propenes → pressure and catalyst → poly(propene)

This is a shorthand way of showing polymer chains. See below for how to draw them.

3) The name of the polymer comes from the type of monomer it's made from — you just put brackets around it and stick the word "poly" in front of it. So propene becomes poly(propene), etc.

4) To get the formula of the polymer, you just put the formula of the monomer in brackets and put a little 'n' after it. So C_3H_6 becomes $(C_3H_6)_n$. Simple.

You Can Draw the Repeat Unit of a Polymer

1) Drawing the displayed formula of an addition polymer from the displayed formula of its monomer is easy. Join the carbons together in a row with no double bonds between them, stick a pair of brackets around the repeating bit, and put an 'n' after it (to show that there are lots of monomers). You should also draw a bond from each of the two carbons in the chain that pass through the brackets — this shows the chain continues.

Chloroethene → Poly(chloroethene)

2) To get from the displayed formula of the polymer to the displayed formula of the monomer, just do the reverse. Draw out the repeating bit of the polymer, get rid of the two bonds going out through the brackets and put a double bond between the carbons.

Poly(tetrafluoroethene) → Tetrafluoroethene

Most Polymers are Hard to Get Rid Of

1) Most addition polymers are inert — they don't react easily. This is because the carbon-carbon bonds in the polymer chain are very strong and aren't easily broken.

2) This means that it takes a really long time for addition polymers to biodegrade (be broken down by bacteria or other organisms) — if you bury them in a landfill site, they'll still be there years later.

3) Burning plastics can release toxic gases, so that's not a great idea either.

4) So it's difficult to dispose of polymers. The best thing is to reuse them as many times as possible and then recycle them if you can.

Which polymer is good for making a cuppa? Poly(putthekettleon)...

Make sure you know how to draw the displayed formulas of addition polymers from the monomer and vice versa.

Q1   Draw the displayed formula of the polymer that is formed when monomers of but-1-ene (shown on the right) are reacted together.   [1 mark]

Polyesters

Polyesters are polymers that contain ester links that join together <u>repeating units</u>.
Oh yeah, it's about to get into the exciting world of <u>condensation polymerisation</u>.

Polymers Can be Made by Condensation Polymerisation

1) <u>Condensation polymerisation</u> usually involves <u>two different types</u> of monomer.

2) The monomers react together and <u>bonds</u> form between them, making polymer chains.

3) Each monomer has to contain at least <u>two functional groups</u>, one on each end of the molecule.

4) Each functional group can react with the functional group of another monomer, creating long chains of alternating monomers. For <u>each new bond</u> that forms, a <u>small molecule</u> (e.g. water) is <u>lost</u>.

Polyesters are Condensation Polymers

The blocks represent the rest of each molecule

1) <u>Polyesters</u> form when <u>dicarboxylic acid monomers</u> and <u>diol monomers</u> react together.

$$n \begin{array}{c} O \\ \| \\ C \\ HO \end{array} \blacksquare \begin{array}{c} O \\ \| \\ C \\ OH \end{array} + n \; HO - \begin{array}{c} H \\ | \\ C \\ | \\ H \end{array} \blacksquare \begin{array}{c} H \\ | \\ C \\ | \\ H \end{array} - OH \longrightarrow \left[\begin{array}{c} O \\ \| \\ C \end{array} \blacksquare \begin{array}{c} O \\ \| \\ C \end{array} - O - \begin{array}{c} H \\ | \\ C \\ | \\ H \end{array} \blacksquare \begin{array}{c} H \\ | \\ C \\ | \\ H \end{array} - O \right]_n + 2n \; H_2O$$

Dicarboxylic acid monomer   Diol monomer   Polyester   Water

<u>Example:</u>

$$n \begin{array}{c} O \\ \| \\ C \\ HO \end{array} \begin{array}{c} O \\ \| \\ C \\ OH \end{array} + n \; HO - \begin{array}{c} H \\ | \\ C \\ | \\ H \end{array} \begin{array}{c} H \\ | \\ C \\ | \\ H \end{array} - OH \longrightarrow \left[\begin{array}{c} O \\ \| \\ C \end{array} \begin{array}{c} O \\ \| \\ C \end{array} - O - \begin{array}{c} H \\ | \\ C \\ | \\ H \end{array} \begin{array}{c} H \\ | \\ C \\ | \\ H \end{array} - O \right]_n + 2n \; H_2O$$

Ethanedioic acid   Ethanediol   Poly(ethyl ethanoate)   Water

You may see polymers shown using their structural formula, e.g.

$$\left[\begin{array}{c} O \\ \| \\ C \end{array} \begin{array}{c} O \\ \| \\ C \end{array} - O - CH_2CH_2 - O \right]_n$$

2) The <u>dicarboxylic acid monomers</u> contain <u>two carboxylic acid</u> (-COOH) groups and the <u>diol monomers</u> contain <u>two alcohol</u> (-OH) groups. There's more on alcohols on page 75 and carboxylic acids on page 77.

3) When the carboxylic acid group reacts with the alcohol group, it forms an <u>ester link</u>.

4) Polyesters are <u>condensation polymers</u> — each time an ester link is formed, a molecule of <u>water</u> is <u>lost</u>.

Some Polyesters are Biodegradable

Nope, no biopolyesters in there.

1) <u>Biodegradable polyesters</u>, known as <u>biopolyesters</u>, can be <u>broken down</u> by bacteria and other living organisms in the environment over time.

2) This means they <u>decompose</u> and don't stay in landfill forever, reducing the polymers' <u>pollutant effect</u>.

Revision's like polymers — it's all about stringing facts together...

...and can go on and on and on and on. Best try some revision now and see if you can answer the questions below.

Q1   Name the two types of monomer that react together to form polyesters.   [2 marks]

Q2   What other molecule is made during the reaction to form polyesters?   [1 mark]

Revision Questions for Section 6

Woohoo — you did it. But before you run off, time to have a go at a few questions.

- Try these questions and <u>tick off each one</u> when you <u>get it right</u>.
- When you've done <u>all the questions</u> for a topic and are <u>completely happy</u> with it, tick off the topic.

Formulae, Names and Isomers (p.67-69) ☑

1) Give the name of the type of formula shown
   a) C_2H_4 b) CH_2CH_2
2) What is a homologous series?
3) Give the stem of the name of a hydrocarbon that contains 5 carbon atoms.

Hydrocarbons (p.70-74) ☑

4) What is crude oil?
5) How do the boiling points of hydrocarbons change as the chain length gets longer?
6) a) What is cracking?
   b) Why do we need to crack hydrocarbons?
7) Write out the word equation for the complete combustion of a hydrocarbon.
8) Explain why carbon monoxide is poisonous.
9) Describe how acid rain is formed.
10) What is the general formula of alkanes?
11) a) Write out the equation for the reaction between methane and bromine in the presence of UV light.
    b) Give the names of the products of this reaction.
12) Explain why alkenes are known as unsaturated molecules.
13) What is the general formula of an alkene?
14) Write out the equation for the reaction between ethene and bromine.

Alcohols, Carboxylic Acids and Esters (p.75-78) ☑

15) State the names of the first four alcohols.
16) Give three ways that alcohols can be oxidised.
17) What type of reaction occurs between ethene and steam?
18) What are the ideal conditions for the fermentation of sugar by yeast to take place at?
19) Give the structural formula of the functional group in carboxylic acids.
20) What ester is produced when ethanol and ethanoic acid react together in the presence of an acid catalyst?
21) Give two uses of esters.

Polymers (p.79-80) ☑

22) a) What kind of polymers are made from monomers with a carbon-carbon double bond?
    b) Give two problems associated with the disposal of these polymers.
23) What type of polymerisation produces polyesters?

Experimental Know-How

Pro scientists need to know how to plan and carry out scientific experiments. They also need to know how to interpret and evaluate the data they get from those experiments. Unluckily for you, those pesky examiners think you should be able to do the same — don't worry though, that's what this topic's all about.

You Might Get Asked Questions on Reliability and Validity

1) RELIABLE results come from experiments that give the same data:

 - each time the experiment is repeated (by you),
 - each time the experiment is reproduced by other scientists.

2) VALID results are both reliable AND come from experiments that were designed to be a fair test.

In the exam, you could be asked to suggest ways to improve the reliability or validity of some experimental results. If so, there are a couple of things to think about:

Controlling Variables Improves Validity

1) A variable is something that has the potential to change, e.g. temperature.
   In a lab experiment you usually change one variable and measure how it affects another variable.

> Example: you might change only the temperature of a chemical reaction and measure how this affects the rate of reaction.

2) To make it a fair test, everything else that could affect the results should stay the same — otherwise you can't tell if the thing you're changing is causing the results or not.

> Example continued: you need to keep the concentration of the reactants the same, otherwise you won't know if any change in the rate of reaction is caused by the change in temperature, or a difference in reactant concentration.

3) The variable you CHANGE is called the INDEPENDENT variable.
4) The variable you MEASURE is called the DEPENDENT variable.
5) The variables that you KEEP THE SAME are called CONTROL variables.

> Example continued:
> Independent variable = temperature
> Dependent variable = rate of reaction
> Control variables = concentration of reactants, volume/mass of reactants, etc.

6) Because you can't always control all the variables, you often need to use a CONTROL EXPERIMENT — an experiment that's kept under the same conditions as the rest of the investigation, but doesn't have anything done to it. This is so that you can see what happens when you don't change anything at all.

Carrying Out Repeats Improves Reliability

1) To improve reliability you need to repeat any measurements you make and calculate the mean (average).
2) You need to repeat each measurement at least three times.

Reliable results — they won't ever forget your birthday...

A typical exam question might describe an experiment, then ask you to suggest what variables need to be controlled. Don't panic, just use your scientific knowledge and a bit of common sense, e.g. if the experiment involves paper chromatography, you know that it's affected by the solvent and the paper you use, so these variables need to be kept constant (providing you're not actually investigating one of them). You might also need to say how you'd control the variables, e.g. the temperature of a reaction could be controlled using a water bath.

More Experimental Know-How

Thought you knew <u>everything</u> there was to know about experiments? <u>Think again</u> my friend...

You Might Have to Suggest Ways to Make an Experiment Safer

1) It's important that experiments are safe. If you're asked to suggest ways to make an experiment safer, you'll first need to identify what the <u>potential hazards</u> might be. Hazards include things like:

- <u>Chemicals</u>, e.g. sulfuric acid can burn your skin and alcohols catch fire easily.
- <u>Fire</u>, e.g. an unattended Bunsen burner is a fire hazard.
- <u>Electricity</u>, e.g. faulty electrical equipment could give you a shock.

2) Then you'll need to suggest ways of <u>reducing</u> the <u>risks</u> involved with the hazard, e.g.

- If you're working with <u>sulfuric acid</u>, always wear gloves and safety goggles. This will reduce the risk of the acid coming into contact with your skin and eyes.
- If you're using a <u>Bunsen burner</u>, stand it on a heat proof mat. This will reduce the risk of starting a fire.
- If you're working with <u>chemicals</u> that give off <u>harmful gases</u>, you need to use a fume cupboard. This will reduce the risk of you breathing in the gases.

You can find out about potential hazards by looking in textbooks, doing some internet research, or asking your teacher.

You Could be Asked About Accuracy...

1) It's important that results are <u>accurate</u>. Accurate results are those that are <u>really close</u> to the <u>true answer</u>.

2) The accuracy of your results usually depends on your <u>method</u>.

E.g. say you wanted to measure the <u>rate</u> of a <u>chemical reaction</u> that releases a <u>gas</u> as a product. The rate of the reaction would be the <u>amount of gas produced per unit time</u>. You could <u>estimate</u> how much gas is produced by <u>counting</u> the number of <u>bubbles</u> that are released. But the bubbles could be <u>different sizes</u>, and if they're produced really quickly you might <u>miss some</u> when counting. It would be more accurate to <u>collect the gas</u> (e.g. using a gas syringe) and <u>measure</u> its <u>volume</u>.

3) To make sure your results are as <u>accurate</u> as possible, you need to make sure you're measuring the <u>right thing</u> and that you <u>don't miss</u> anything or <u>include</u> anything that shouldn't be included in the measurements.

E.g. if you're measuring the volume of gas produced using a gas syringe, you need to make sure the syringe is <u>empty</u> at the start of the experiment. If there's any air in it the reading will be <u>wrong</u>.

...And Precision

Results also need to be <u>precise</u>. Precise results are ones where the data is <u>all really close</u> to the <u>mean</u> (average) of your repeated results (i.e. not spread out).

Repeat	Data set 1	Data set 2
1	12	11
2	14	17
3	13	14
Mean	13	14

Data set 1 is more precise than data set 2.

Sometimes, results are described as precise if they've been taken using sensitive instruments that can measure in small increments, e.g. using a ruler with a millimetre scale gives more precise data than a ruler with a scale in centimetres.

Not revising — an unacceptable exam hazard...

It may interest you to know that you won't just have to write about other people's experiments in the exam. Sometimes you'll be asked to describe how you'd carry out your own experiment and all this stuff about reliability and what not will apply then too. Ah. From the look on your face, I'm guessing it didn't interest you to know that.

Drawing Graphs and Interpreting Results

Processing your data means doing some calculations with it to make it more useful. Once you've done that, you can present your results in a nice chart or graph to help you spot any patterns in your data.

You Should Be Able to Identify Anomalous Results

1) Most results vary a bit, but any that are totally different are called anomalous results.

2) They're caused by human errors, e.g. by a mistake made when measuring or by not setting up a piece of equipment properly.

3) You could be asked to identify an anomalous result in the exam and suggest what caused it — just look for a result that doesn't fit in with the rest (e.g. it's too high or too low) then try to figure out what could have gone wrong with the experiment to have caused it.

4) If you're calculating an average, you can ignore any anomalous results.

You Might Have to Process Your Data

1) When you've done repeats of an experiment you should always calculate the mean (average). To do this add together all the data values and divide by the total number of values in the sample.

2) You might also need to calculate the range (how spread out the data is). To do this find the largest number and subtract the smallest number from it.

Ignore anomalous results when calculating these.

Example: The results of an experiment to find the mass of gas lost from two reactions are shown below. Calculate the mean and the range for the mass of gas lost in each reaction.

Test tube	Repeat 1 (g)	Repeat 2 (g)	Repeat 3 (g)	Mean (g)	Range (g)
A	28	37	32	(28 + 37 + 32) ÷ 3 = 32	37 − 28 = 9
B	47	51	60	(47 + 51 + 60) ÷ 3 = 53	60 − 47 = 13

Bar Charts can be Used to Show Different Types of Data

Bar charts can be used to display:

1) Categoric data — data that comes in distinct categories, e.g. alkane chain length, metals.

2) Discrete data — data that can be counted in chunks, where there's no in-between value, e.g. number of protons is discrete because you can't have half a proton.

3) Continuous data — numerical data that can have any value in a range, e.g. length, volume, temperature.

There are some golden rules you need to follow for drawing bar charts:

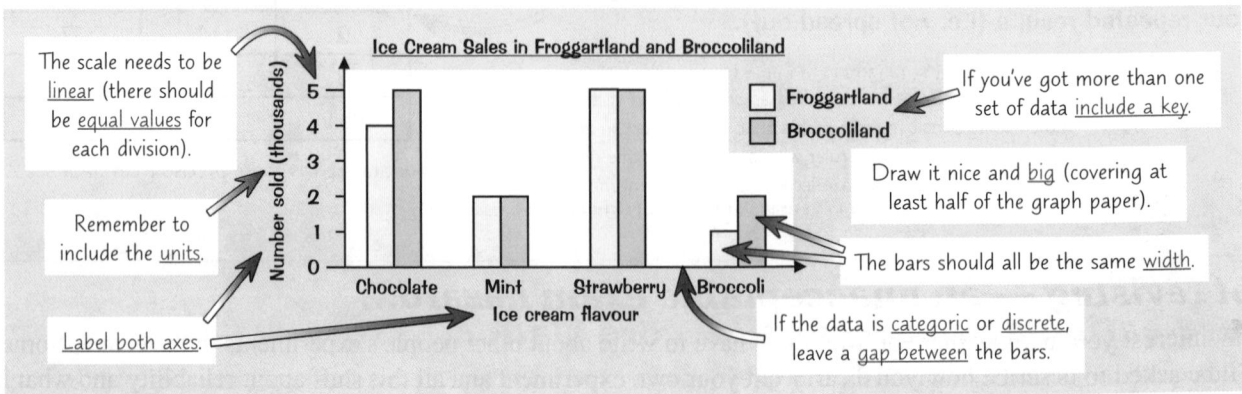

The scale needs to be linear (there should be equal values for each division).

Remember to include the units.

Label both axes.

If you've got more than one set of data include a key.

Draw it nice and big (covering at least half of the graph paper).

The bars should all be the same width.

If the data is categoric or discrete, leave a gap between the bars.

Graphs can be Used to Plot Continuous Data

If both variables are <u>continuous</u> you should use a <u>graph</u> to display the data.

Here are the rules for plotting points on a graph:

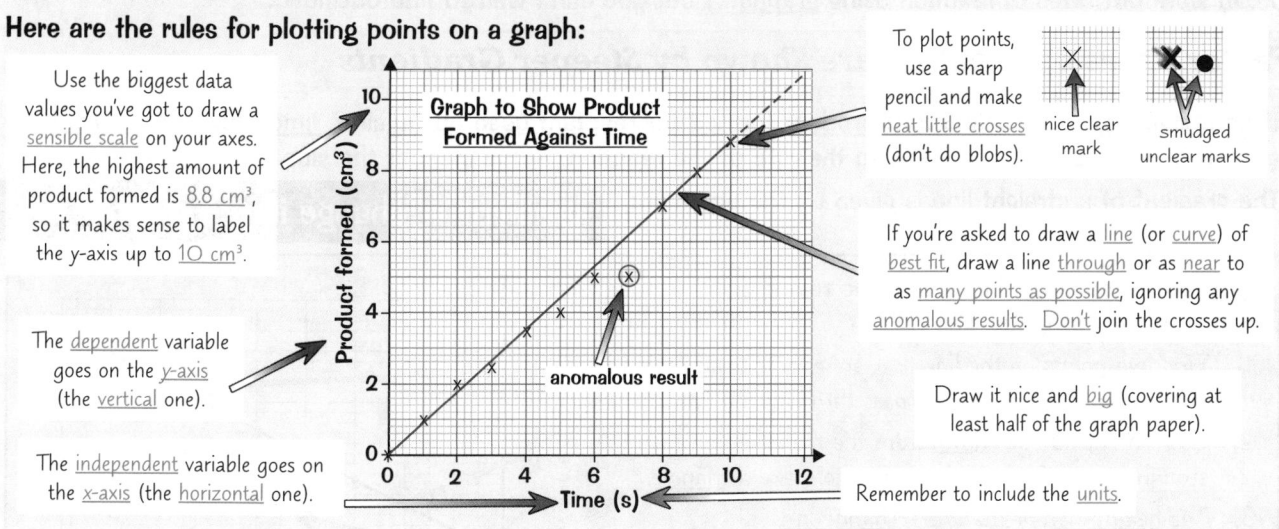

Use the biggest data values you've got to draw a <u>sensible scale</u> on your axes. Here, the highest amount of product formed is <u>8.8 cm³</u>, so it makes sense to label the y-axis up to <u>10 cm³</u>.

The <u>dependent</u> variable goes on the <u>y-axis</u> (the <u>vertical</u> one).

The <u>independent</u> variable goes on the x-axis (the <u>horizontal</u> one).

To plot points, use a sharp pencil and make <u>neat little crosses</u> (don't do blobs). nice clear mark — smudged unclear marks

If you're asked to draw a <u>line</u> (or <u>curve</u>) of <u>best fit</u>, draw a line <u>through</u> or as <u>near</u> to as <u>many points as possible</u>, ignoring any <u>anomalous results</u>. <u>Don't</u> join the crosses up.

Draw it nice and <u>big</u> (covering at least half of the graph paper).

Remember to include the <u>units</u>.

You Need to be Able to Interpret Graphs

1) A graph is used to show the <u>relationship</u> between two variables — you need to be able to look at a graph and <u>describe</u> this relationship.

> E.g. the graph above shows that as <u>time goes on</u>, <u>more product is formed</u> and that the amount of product formed is <u>directly proportional</u> to time.

A relationship is directly proportional if one variable increases at the same rate as the other variable (so if one variable doubles, the other also doubles, etc.). A graph shows direct proportion when the line is straight and goes through the origin (O,O).

2) You also need to be able to <u>read information</u> off a graph. In this example, if you wanted to know how much product had been formed by <u>11 s</u>, you'd draw a <u>vertical line up</u> to the graph line from the x-axis at 11 s and a <u>horizontal line across</u> to the y-axis. This would tell you that the amount of product formed by 11 s was around <u>9.8 cm³</u>.

Graphs Show the Correlation Between Two Variables

1) You can get <u>three</u> types of <u>correlation</u> (relationship) between variables:

2) Just because there's correlation, it doesn't mean the change in one variable is <u>causing</u> the change in the other — there might be <u>other factors</u> involved.

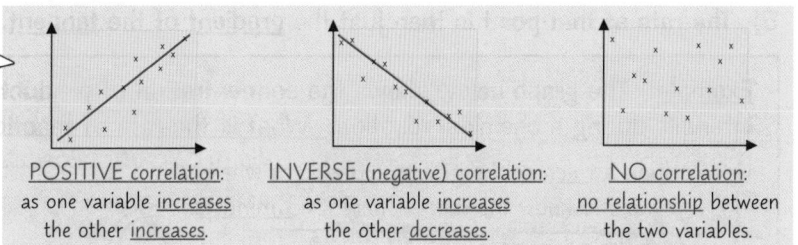

<u>POSITIVE</u> correlation: as one variable <u>increases</u> the other <u>increases</u>.

<u>INVERSE</u> (negative) correlation: as one variable <u>increases</u> the other <u>decreases</u>.

<u>NO</u> correlation: <u>no relationship</u> between the two variables.

3) There are three possible reasons for a correlation:

- <u>CHANCE</u>: It might seem strange, but two things can show a correlation purely due to <u>chance</u>.

- <u>LINKED BY A 3RD VARIABLE</u>: A lot of the time it may <u>look</u> as if a change in one variable is causing a change in the other, but it <u>isn't</u> — a <u>third variable links</u> the two things.

- <u>CAUSE</u>: Sometimes a change in one variable does <u>cause</u> a change in the other. You can only conclude that a correlation is due to cause when you've <u>controlled all the variables</u> that could, just could, be affecting the result.

I love eating apples — I call it core elation...

Science is all about finding relationships between things. And I don't mean that chemists gather together in corners to discuss whether or not Devini and Sebastian might be a couple... though they probably do that too.

Calculating Rates From Graphs

You can work out rates of reaction using <u>graphs</u>. I bet you can't wait to find out how...

Faster Rates of Reaction are Shown by Steeper Gradients

If you have a graph of <u>amount of product formed</u> (or <u>reactant used up</u>) against <u>time</u>, then the <u>gradient</u> (slope) of the graph will be equal to the rate of the reaction — the <u>steeper</u> the slope, the <u>faster</u> the rate.

The gradient of a <u>straight line</u> is given by the equation: **gradient = change in y ÷ change in x**

<u>Example</u>: Calculate the rate of the reaction shown on the graph on the right.

1) Find two <u>points on the line</u> that are <u>easy to read</u> the x and y values of (ones that pass through grid lines).

2) Draw a line straight <u>down</u> from the higher point and straight <u>across</u> from the lower one to make a <u>triangle</u>.

3) The <u>height</u> of your triangle = <u>change in y</u>
   The <u>base</u> of your triangle = <u>change in x</u>
   Change in y = 16 − 5 = 11   Change in x = 65 − 20 = 45

4) Use the formula to work out the <u>gradient</u>, and therefore the rate.
   Gradient = change in y ÷ change in x = 11 ÷ 45 = 0.24 cm³/s

The units of the rate are just "units of y-axis ÷ units of x-axis".

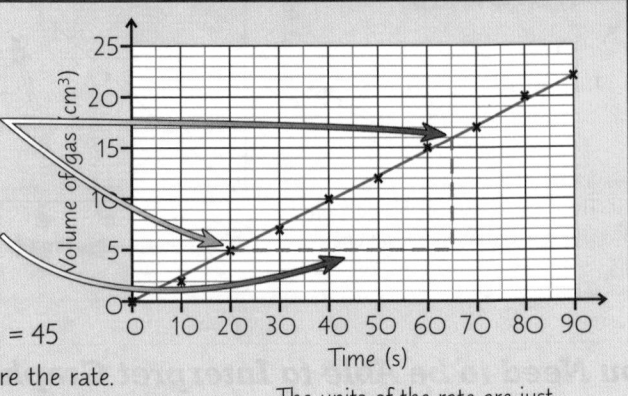

Draw a Tangent to Find the Gradient of a Curve

1) If your graph (or part of it) is a <u>curve</u>, the gradient, and therefore <u>rate</u>, is different at different points along the curve.

2) To find the <u>gradient</u> of the graph at a certain point, you'll have to draw a <u>tangent</u> at that point.

3) A tangent is just a line that <u>touches the curve</u> and has the <u>same gradient</u> as the line at that point.

4) To draw a tangent, place a <u>ruler</u> on the line of best fit at the point you're interested in, so you can see the <u>whole curve</u>. Adjust the ruler so the space between the ruler and the curve is the same on both sides of the point. Draw a line <u>along the ruler</u> to make the <u>tangent</u>.

5) The rate at that point is then just the <u>gradient</u> of the <u>tangent</u>.

Tangent at 40 s.

<u>Example</u>: The graph below shows the concentration of product formed, measured at regular intervals during a chemical reaction. What is the rate of reaction at 3 minutes?

1) Position a <u>ruler</u> on the graph at the point where you want to know the rate — here it's <u>3 minutes</u>.

2) Adjust the ruler until the <u>space</u> between the ruler and the curve is <u>equal</u> on <u>both sides</u> of the point.

3) Draw a line along the ruler to make the <u>tangent</u>. Extend the line <u>right</u> <u>across</u> the graph.

4) Pick <u>two points</u> on the line that are easy to read. Use them to calculate the <u>gradient</u> of the tangent in order to find the <u>rate</u>:

gradient = change in y ÷ change in x
= (0.22 − 0.14) ÷ (5.0 − 2.0)
= 0.08 ÷ 3.0
= 0.027

So, the rate of reaction at 3 minutes was 0.027 mol/dm³/min.

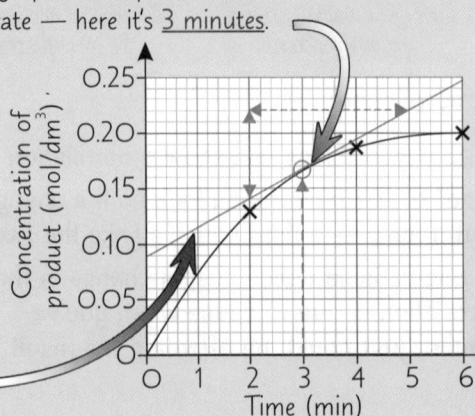

I saw my chemistry teacher on holiday — he was a tanned gent...

Lots of nifty graph skills here. Gradients aren't too hard, but make sure those tangents don't trip you up.

Planning Experiments

In the exam, you could be asked to <u>plan</u> or <u>describe</u> how you'd <u>carry out</u> an experiment. The experiment might be one you've already come across (easy) or (gasp) you might be asked to come up with an <u>experiment of your own</u> to test something. I know. Examiners are <u>harsh</u>. It's not as bad as it sounds though.

You Need to Be Able to Plan a Good Experiment

Here are some <u>general tips</u> on what to include when planning an experiment:

1) Say <u>what</u> you're <u>measuring</u> (i.e. what the <u>dependent variable</u> is going to be).

2) Say <u>what</u> you're <u>changing</u> (i.e. what the <u>independent variable</u> is going to be) and describe <u>how</u> you're going to change it.

3) Describe the <u>method</u> and the <u>apparatus</u> you'd use.

4) Describe what <u>variables</u> you're keeping <u>constant</u> — and <u>how</u> you're going to do it.

5) Say that you need to <u>repeat</u> the experiment at least three times, to make the results <u>more reliable</u>.

6) Say whether you're using a <u>control</u> or not.

Here's an <u>idea</u> of the sort of thing you might be asked in the exam and what you might write as an answer...

> Even if you can't remember all the details of an experimental method you've learned about, you could still get marks for describing things like the independent and dependent variables.

Exam-style Question:

1 Describe an experiment to investigate the effect of concentration on the reaction of dilute hydrochloric acid and magnesium metal. **(6 marks)**

Example Answer:

In this experiment you should change the concentration of the dilute hydrochloric acid. You can see what effect this has by measuring the mass of the reaction mixture.

Set up a flask containing a measured mass of magnesium metal. Place the flask on a mass balance.

Pour a measured volume of dilute hydrochloric acid into the flask and start the timer. Take readings of the mass at regular time intervals until the mass doesn't change anymore. The mass of gas lost from the reaction mixture can be calculated using this data.

Carry out the experiment again with different concentrations of dilute hydrochloric acid (e.g. 0.1 mol/dm^3, 0.2 mol/dm^3, 0.3 mol/dm^3 and 0.4 mol/dm^3).

The mass should be measured at the same time intervals for each acid concentration. The volume of acid should always be the same and the same mass of magnesium metal should be used each time. The temperature must also remain constant.

Repeat the experiment three times at each acid concentration and use the results to find the average mass of gas lost at each time interval for each concentration.

> You could also collect the hydrogen in a gas syringe and measure its volume.

I'm thinking of throwing a surprise party for Saturn.

Make sure you planet first...

Experiments Test Hypotheses

1) A <u>hypothesis</u> is a possible <u>explanation</u> for something that you've observed.

2) You can use experiments to <u>test</u> whether a hypothesis might be <u>right or not</u>. This involves making a <u>prediction</u> based on the hypothesis and testing it by <u>gathering evidence</u> (i.e. <u>data</u>) from <u>investigations</u>. If <u>evidence</u> from <u>experiments</u> backs up a prediction, you're a step closer to figuring out if the hypothesis is true.

Plan your way to exam success...

The number of marks available for a question like the one above will vary, but it'll usually be around five or six. This means you'll have to write an extended answer. Think about what you're going to say beforehand and in what order — that way you're less likely to forget something important. Like what it is you're actually measuring, say.

Conclusions and Evaluations

Congratulations — you're nearly at the end of a gruelling investigation, time to <u>draw conclusions</u> and <u>evaluate</u>.

You Can Only Conclude What the Data Shows and NO MORE

1) Drawing conclusions might seem pretty straightforward — you just <u>look at your data</u> and <u>say what pattern or relationship you see</u> between the dependent and independent variables.

	Catalyst	Rate of reaction (cm^3/s)

The table on the right shows the rate of a reaction in the presence of two <u>different catalysts</u>.

<u>CONCLUSION</u>: Catalyst <u>B</u> makes <u>this reaction</u> go faster than catalyst A.

Catalyst	Rate of reaction (cm^3/s)
A	13.5
B	19.5
No catalyst	5.5

2) But you've got to be really careful that your conclusion <u>matches the data</u> you've got and <u>doesn't go any further</u>.

> You <u>can't</u> conclude that catalyst B increases the rate of <u>any other reaction</u> more than catalyst A — the results might be completely different.

3) You also need to be able to <u>use your results</u> to <u>justify your conclusion</u> (i.e. back up your conclusion with some specific data).

> The rate of this reaction was <u>6 cm^3/s faster</u> using catalyst B compared with catalyst A.

4) When writing a conclusion you need to <u>refer back</u> to the original hypothesis and say whether the data <u>supports it</u> or not.

> The <u>hypothesis</u> for this experiment might have been that adding a catalyst would <u>increase the rate of reaction</u> because it would <u>decrease</u> the <u>activation energy</u>. The <u>prediction</u> may have been that <u>catalyst B</u> would decrease the activation energy by a greater amount so would <u>increase the rate of reaction more</u> than catalyst A. If so, the data <u>supports</u> the hypothesis.

5) You could also make more <u>predictions</u> based on your conclusion, then <u>further experiments</u> could be carried out to test them.

Evaluations — Describe How it Could be Improved

An evaluation is a <u>critical analysis</u> of the whole investigation.

1) You should comment on the <u>method</u> — was it <u>valid</u>? Did you control all the other variables to make it a <u>fair test</u>?

2) Comment on the <u>quality</u> of the <u>results</u> — was there <u>enough evidence</u> to reach a valid <u>conclusion</u>? Were the results <u>reliable</u>, <u>valid</u>, <u>accurate</u> and <u>precise</u>?

3) Were there any <u>anomalous</u> results? If there were <u>none</u> then <u>say so</u>. If there were any, try to <u>explain</u> them — were they caused by <u>errors</u> in measurement? Were there any other <u>variables</u> that could have <u>affected</u> the results?

4) All this analysis will allow you to say how <u>confident</u> you are that your conclusion is <u>right</u>.

5) Then you can suggest any <u>changes</u> to the <u>method</u> that would <u>improve</u> the quality of the results, so that you could have <u>more confidence</u> in your conclusion. For example, you might suggest <u>changing</u> the way you controlled a variable, or <u>increasing</u> the number of <u>measurements</u> you took. Taking more measurements at <u>narrower intervals</u> could give you a <u>more accurate result</u>. For example:

> <u>Enzymes</u> have an <u>optimum temperature</u> (a temperature at which they <u>work best</u>). Say you do an experiment to find an enzyme's optimum temperature and take measurements at 10 °C, 20 °C, 30 °C, 40 °C and 50 °C. The results of this experiment tell you the optimum is <u>40 °C</u>. You could then <u>repeat</u> the experiment, taking <u>more measurements around 40 °C</u> to get a <u>more accurate</u> value for the optimum.

6) You could also make more <u>predictions</u> based on your conclusion, then <u>further experiments</u> could be carried out to test them.

When suggesting improvements to the investigation, always make sure that you say why you think this would make the results better.

Evaluation — next time, I'll make sure I don't burn the lab down...

And that's a wrap. Well, not quite. You've still got the small matter of the whole exam shenanigans to look forward to. Around 20% of your marks will come from being able to describe experiments, and analysing and evaluating data and methods in an appropriate way — so, make sure you're happy with everything in this section. Best of luck.

Answers

Section 1 — Particles and Mixtures

Page 2 — States of Matter
Q1 From a gas to a liquid *[1 mark]*.

Page 3 — Movement of Particles
Q1 The purple colour from the potassium manganate(VII) slowly spreads out *[1 mark]*. This is because the potassium manganate(VII) particles are diffusing out among the particles of water *[1 mark]*.

Page 4 — Solutions
Q1 A solute is a substance that is being dissolved *[1 mark]*, and a solvent is a solution/liquid that a solute dissolves in to *[1 mark]*.
Q2 The ability of a substance to dissolve in a solvent *[1 mark]*.

Page 5 — Investigating Solubility
Q1 Make a saturated solution of the solid in a boiling tube *[1 mark]*. Stir the solution and place the boiling tube in a water bath set to 40 °C for 5 minutes *[1 mark]*. Pour some of the solution into a pre-weighed evaporating basin and re-weigh the basin and its contents *[1 mark]*. Heat the evaporating basin until all the water has evaporated, and re-weigh the basin and its contents *[1 mark]*. The solubility could be found by dividing the mass of solid left in the basin by the mass of water removed during evaporation *[1 mark]*.

Page 6 — Atoms
Q1 electrons = 19 *[1 mark]*, protons = 19 *[1 mark]*, neutrons = 39 − 19 = 20 *[1 mark]*.

Page 7 — Isotopes and Relative Atomic Mass
Q1 (79 × 51) + (81 × 49) = 7998 *[1 mark]*
7998 ÷ 100 = 79.98 = 80 *[1 mark]*

Page 8 — Elements, Compounds and Mixtures
Q1a) compound *[1 mark]*
b) element *[1 mark]*
c) mixture *[1 mark]*

Page 9 — Filtration and Crystallisation
Q1 Slowly heat the solution to evaporate off some of the water *[1 mark]*. Stop heating once some of the water has evaporated / once copper sulfate crystals start to form *[1 mark]*. Allow the solution to cool until copper sulfate crystals form *[1 mark]*. Filter the crystals out of the solution and dry them in a warm place / desiccator / drying oven *[1 mark]*.

Page 10 — Chromatography
Q1 R_f of Y = distance travelled by Y ÷ distance travelled by solvent
= 3.6 cm ÷ 6.0 cm *[1 mark]* = 0.60 *[1 mark]*

Page 11 — Distillation
Q1 Methanol will be collected in the first fraction *[1 mark]*, because it has the lowest boiling point of the three compounds in the mixture and so will evaporate first *[1 mark]*.

Section 2 — The Periodic Table and Bonding

Page 13 — The Periodic Table
Q1 Potassium and sodium are both in Group 1. Potassium and calcium are in different groups. So the properties of potassium should be closer to those of sodium than calcium *[1 mark]*, because elements in the same group have similar properties *[1 mark]*.

Page 14 — Electron Shells
Q1 2.8.3 or

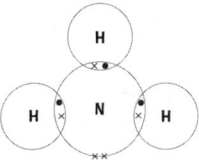

[1 mark]

Page 15 — More on the Periodic Table
Q1 solution A *[1 mark]*
Q2 Group 0 elements are inert/unreactive *[1 mark]*. This is because they have a full outer shell of electrons *[1 mark]*.

Page 16 — Ionic Bonding
Q1a) 1+ *[1 mark]*
b) 2− *[1 mark]*
c) 1− *[1 mark]*
Q2 Each sodium atom loses an electron to form an Na^+ ion *[1 mark]*. Each chlorine atom gains an electron to form a Cl^- ion *[1 mark]*. The oppositely charged ions are attracted to each other by electrostatic attraction *[1 mark]*.

Page 17 — Ionic Compounds
Q1 A lot of energy is needed to break the strong attraction between the ions/the strong ionic bonds *[1 mark]*.

Page 18 — Covalent Bonding
Q1 two *[1 mark]*
Q2

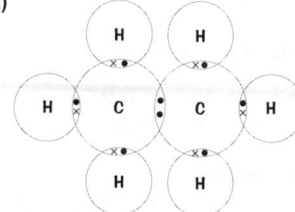

[1 mark for all bonding pairs of electrons correct. 1 mark for non-bonding pair correct.]

Page 19 — More on Covalent Bonding
Q1a)

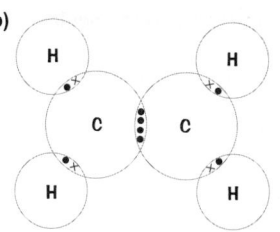

[1 mark for all bonding pairs of electrons correct. 1 mark for no extra electrons shown.]

b)

[1 mark for all bonding pairs of electrons correct. 1 mark for no extra electrons shown.]

Page 20 — Covalent Substances
Q1 Graphite contains free/delocalised electrons, which can carry an electric current *[1 mark]*. Diamond does not contain any free/delocalised electrons *[1 mark]*.

Page 21 — Electrical Conductivity and Metals
Q1 The layers of ions in a metal can slide over each other *[1 mark]*.
Q2 Copper is a good electrical conductor *[1 mark]* as it contains delocalised electrons which are able to carry an electrical current *[1 mark]*.

Section 3 — Equations, Calculations and Electrolysis

Page 23 — Balancing Equations
Q1 $2Fe + 3Cl_2 \rightarrow 2FeCl_3$ *[1 mark]*
Q2a) water → hydrogen + oxygen *[1 mark]*
b) $2H_2O \rightarrow 2H_2 + O_2$
[1 mark for correct reactants and products, 1 mark for a correctly balanced equation]

Page 24 — Relative Formula Mass
Q1a) A_r of C = 12
A_r of H = 1
A_r of O = 16
M_r of C_2H_5OH = (12 × 2) + (1 × 5) + 16 + 1 = 46 *[1 mark]*
b) A_r of C = 12
A_r of H = 1
A_r of N = 14
M_r of $C_6H_5NH_2$ = (12 × 6) + (1 × 5) + 14 + (1 × 2) = 93 *[1 mark]*

Page 25 — Moles
Q1 moles = mass ÷ M_r
= 90 ÷ 18 = 5 moles *[1 mark]*
Q2 mass = moles × M_r
= 2.2 × 100 = 220 g *[1 mark]*

Page 26 — Calculating Masses in Reactions
Q1a) M_r(KBr) = 39 + 80 = 119
$M_r(Br_2)$ = 80 × 2 = 160 *[1 mark]*
moles of KBr = mass ÷ M_r = 23.8 ÷ 119 = 0.200 moles *[1 mark]*
From the equation, 2 moles of KBr react to produce 1 mole of Br_2. So 0.200 moles of KBr will produce (0.200 ÷ 2) = 0.100 moles of Br_2 *[1 mark]*.
So mass of Br_2 = 0.100 × 160 = 16.0 g *[1 mark]*
b) Percentage yield = actual yield ÷ theoretical yield × 100 = 12.4 g ÷ 16.0 g × 100 *[1 mark]* = 77.5% *[1 mark]*

Answers

Page 27 — Empirical and Molecular Formulae

Q1 mass of oxygen = 45.6 − 13.9 = 31.7 g
[1 mark]
moles = mass ÷ M_r
moles of oxygen = 31.7 ÷ 16 = 1.98125
moles of nitrogen = 13.9 ÷ 14 = 0.99...
[1 mark]
Divide by the smallest number (0.99...).
oxygen = 1.98125 ÷ 0.99... = 2
nitrogen = 0.99... ÷ 0.99... = 1
Ratio of O : N = 2 : 1.
So empirical formula = NO_2 *[1 mark]*

Page 28 — Finding Formulae Using Experiments

Q1 Heat a crucible until it's red hot, leave it to cool, and then weigh it, along with its lid *[1 mark]*. Add a sample of the metal that you're investigating and reweigh the crucible, lid and contents *[1 mark]*. Heat the crucible strongly for around 10 minutes *[1 mark]*. Allow the crucible to cool and reweigh the crucible, lid and contents *[1 mark]*.

Page 29 — Water of Crystallisation

Q1 The water contained in a salt lattice *[1 mark]*.

Page 30 — Moles and Concentration

Q1 200 cm³ = (200 ÷ 1000) dm³ = 0.20 dm³
[1 mark]
moles = concentration × volume
= 0.55 × 0.20 = 0.11 moles *[1 mark]*

Page 31 — Calculating Volume

Q1 moles = mass ÷ M_r
moles of CH_4 = 36 ÷ 16 = 2.25 moles
volume = moles × 24 = 2.25 × 24 = 54 dm³
[2 marks for correct answer, otherwise 1 mark for correct moles of CH_4]

Q2 moles = mass ÷ M_r
moles of Na = 11.5 ÷ 23 = 0.50 moles
From the equation, 2 moles of Na produce 1 mole of H_2, so 0.50 moles of Na produce 0.50 ÷ 2 = 0.25 moles of H_2
volume = moles × 24 = 0.25 × 24 = 6.0 dm³
[3 marks for correct answer, otherwise 1 mark for correct moles of Na, 1 mark for correct moles of gas]

Page 32 — Electrolysis

Q1 the anode *[1 mark]*

Page 33 — Electrolysis of Aqueous Solutions

Q1 Clean the surface of two inert electrodes *[1 mark]*. Place both electrodes in a beaker filled with electrolyte *[1 mark]*. Connect the electrodes to a power supply using crocodile clips and wires *[1 mark]*.

Q2 $2Br^- \rightarrow Br_2 + 2e^-$ *[1 mark for correct formulas, 1 mark for balancing]*

Section 4 — Inorganic Chemistry

Page 35 — Group 1 — The Alkali Metals

Q1 $2K + 2H_2O \rightarrow 2KOH + H_2$ *[1 mark for correct products and reactants and 1 mark for correct balancing]*

Page 36 — Group 7 — The Halogens

Q1 The boiling points increase as you go down the group *[1 mark]*

Page 37 — Displacement Reactions

Q1 He should add a few drops of the solution to a bromine salt solution (e.g. potassium bromide) *[1 mark]*. If the solution turns orange, the halogen solution contains chlorine. If there is no reaction, the halogen solution contains bromine *[1 mark]*.

Page 38 — Gases in the Atmosphere

Q1 Nitrogen, oxygen, argon and CO_2 *[1 mark]*

Q2 Iron and phosphorus can react with oxygen so they remove it from the air *[1 mark]*. The volume of oxygen removed from the air can be measured and therefore the percentage of oxygen calculated *[1 mark]*.

Page 39 — Gases in Reactions

Q1 sulfur dioxide/SO_2 *[1 mark]*

Page 40 — Carbon Dioxide

Q1 More CO_2 is being released into the atmosphere than is being removed *[1 mark]*.

Q2 They act like an insulating layer keeping the earth warmer than it would be without them *[1 mark]*. They absorb most of the heat that would normally be radiated out into space, and re-radiate it in all directions *[1 mark]*.

Page 41 — Reactions of Metals

Q1 Metal B, Metal C, Metal A *[1 mark]*

Page 42 — The Reactivity Series

Q1 Silver would not displace iron from iron chloride solution, because it's lower down than iron in the reactivity series/less reactive than iron *[1 mark]*.

Page 43 — Iron

Q1 Magnesium is more reactive than iron *[1 mark]*, so will be oxidised/react with water and oxygen in preference to iron *[1 mark]*.

Q2 Oxygen *[1 mark]*, water *[1 mark]*

Page 44 — Metals and Redox

Q1 Tin is less reactive than carbon *[1 mark]* so you could extract tin from its ore by reducing it with carbon *[1 mark]*.

Page 45 — Uses of Metals

Q1 E.g. car bodies / bridges / cutlery *[1 mark]*

Page 46 — Acids and Alkalis

Q1 Acidic *[1 mark]*

Page 47 — Reactions of Acids

Q1 $2HCl + CaCO_3 \rightarrow CaCl_2 + H_2O + CO_2$
[1 mark for correct reactants and products, 1 mark for balanced equation]

Page 48 — Titrations

Q1 moles of NaOH = 1 × (30 ÷ 1000) = 0.03
1 mole of NaOH reacts with 1 mole of HCl, so 0.03 moles of NaOH must react with 0.03 moles of HCl.
Concentration of HCl = number of moles ÷ volume = 0.03 ÷ (60 ÷ 1000) = 0.5 mol/dm³
[3 marks for the correct answer, otherwise 1 mark for correct moles of HCl and 1 mark for using the correct equation to work out the concentration of HCl.]

Page 49 — Making Insoluble Salts

Q1 a) soluble *[1 mark]*
b) insoluble *[1 mark]*
c) insoluble *[1 mark]*
d) soluble *[1 mark]*

Page 50 — Making Soluble Salts

Q1 E.g. add the base/iron oxide to warmed nitric acid *[1 mark]*. Keep on adding base until all the acid has been neutralised. At this point, no more base will react and it will sink to the bottom of the flask *[1 mark]*. Filter out the excess solid using filter paper *[1 mark]*. Evaporate off some of the water from the salt solution using a Bunsen burner and then leave it to cool until salt crystals form *[1 mark]*. Filter off the crystals and leave them to dry *[1 mark]*.

Page 51 — Tests for Cations

Q1 The compound contains potassium/K^+ ions *[1 mark]*

Q2 The solution contains iron(III)/Fe^{3+} ions *[1 mark]*

Page 52 — Tests for Anions

Q1 The solution contains iodide ions *[1 mark]*

Page 53 — Tests for Gases and Water

Q1 Place a piece of damp red litmus paper in a test tube of the gas. If the litmus paper turns blue then the gas is ammonia *[1 mark]*

Section 5 — Physical Chemistry

Page 55 — Energy Transfer in Reactions

Q1

[1 mark for correct axes, 1 mark for correct energy levels of reactants and products, 1 mark for correct shape of curve linking the reactants to the products]

Page 56 — Measuring Enthalpy Changes

Q1 Some energy is lost to the surroundings *[1 mark]*.

Page 57 — Calculating Enthalpy Changes

Q1 Q = m × c × ΔT
= 40 g × 4.2 J/g/°C × 26 °C *[1 mark]*
= 4368 J *[1 mark]*

Page 58 — Bond Energies

Q1 Energy required to break original bonds:
(1 × N≡N) + (3 × H–H)
= 941 + (3 × 436) = 941 + 1308
= 2249 kJ/mol *[1 mark]*
Energy released by forming new bonds:
(6 × N–H)
= 6 × 391 = 2346 kJ/mol *[1 mark]*
Enthalpy change:
= 2249 − 2346 = −97 kJ/mol *[1 mark]*

Answers

Page 59 — Rates of Reaction
Q1 The activation energy for a reaction is the minimum amount of energy that particles need to react *[1 mark]*.

Page 60 — Factors Affecting the Rate of Reaction
Q1 The energy transferred during a collision (particles must collide with enough energy for the collision to be successful) *[1 mark]* and the collision frequency *[1 mark]*.

Q2 As the temperature increases, the speed that the particles move at increases, so there are more collisions *[1 mark]*. Higher temperatures also increase the energy of the collisions *[1 mark]*. So at higher temperatures there are more successful collisions / more particles collide with enough energy to react *[1 mark]*.

Page 61 — Catalysts
Q1 A catalyst is a substance which increases the rate of reaction *[1 mark]*, without being chemically changed or used up in the reaction *[1 mark]*.

Q2 A catalyst speeds up a reaction by providing an alternative reaction pathway *[1 mark]* with a lower activation energy *[1 mark]*.

Q3 The height of the curve would decrease *[1 mark]*.

Page 62 — Measuring Rates of Reaction
Q1 E.g. put a conical flask on a mass balance and add your reactants *[1 mark]*. As gas is produced from the reaction, measure how quickly the reading on the balance drops until the balance stops changing *[1 mark]*. Plot the results in a graph of change in mass against time *[1 mark]*.

Q2 E.g. the result is subjective *[1 mark]*.

Page 63 — Rate of Reaction Experiments
Q1 E.g. place a measured volume of hydrochloric acid of a known concentration in a conical flask. Add a known mass of calcium carbonate in the form of marble chips *[1 mark]*. Immediately add a gas syringe. Take readings of the volume of gas produced at regular time intervals *[1 mark]*. Repeat the experiment with the same volume and concentration of acid and the same mass of calcium carbonate but increase the surface area of calcium carbonate by crunching the marble up / using powdered chalk *[1 mark]*.

Page 64 — More Rate of Reaction Experiments
Q1 E.g. use a water bath to warm solutions of a known volume of hydrochloric acid and sodium thiosulfate to a certain temperature *[1 mark]*. Mix the two solutions and place the reaction vessel on a piece of paper with a black mark on it *[1 mark]*. Time how long it takes for the black mark to disappear as the precipitate forms *[1 mark]*. Repeat the reaction at different temperatures, keeping the volumes of liquids the same each time *[1 mark]*.

Page 65 — Reversible Reactions
Q1 A reversible reaction is one where the products can react with each other and convert back to the original reactants *[1 mark]*.

Q2 Dynamic equilibrium occurs when the forward and backward reactions in a reversible reaction occur at the same time *[1 mark]* and at the same rate *[1 mark]*, so there is no change in concentration of the reactants or the products *[1 mark]*.

Section 6 — Organic Chemistry

Page 67 — Organic Compounds
Q1 A functional group is a group of atoms that determine how a compound typically reacts *[1 mark]*.

Page 68 — Naming Organic Compounds
Q1 but-2-ene *[1 mark]*

Page 69 — Isomers
Q1 Two molecules are isomers of each other if they have the same molecular formula but the atoms are arranged differently / they have a different structural formula *[1 mark]*.

Page 70 — Crude Oil
Q1 Hydrocarbons are molecules made of only carbon and hydrogen *[1 mark]*.

Q2 Crude oil is heated until most of it turns into a gas *[1 mark]*. The gases enter a fractionating column and the liquid part/ bitumen is drained off at the bottom *[1 mark]*. There's a temperature gradient in the column — the column is hot at the bottom and cooler at the top *[1 mark]*. The longer hydrocarbons with high boiling points turn back into liquids/condense and drain out lower down the column *[1 mark]*. Shorter hydrocarbons have lower boiling points so turn into liquids and are drained off higher up the column *[1 mark]*.

Page 71 — Cracking
Q1 600 °C — 700 °C *[1 mark]*
Q2 alkanes *[1 mark]*, alkenes *[1 mark]*

Page 72 — Burning Hydrocarbons
Q1 carbon monoxide/CO *[1 mark]*, carbon/C *[1 mark]*

Page 73 — Alkanes
Q1 E.g.

[1 mark]

Page 74 — Alkenes
Q1 The general formula of an alkene is C_nH_{2n}. In this case, n = 10, so the molecular formula is $C_{10}H_{(2 \times 10)} = C_{10}H_{20}$ *[1 mark]*.

Page 75 — Alcohols
Q1 methanol *[1 mark]*
Q2 potassium dichromate(VI) in dilute sulfuric acid *[1 mark]*

Page 76 — Production of Ethanol
Q1 sugars/glucose *[1 mark]*
Q2 Yeast contains an enzyme which speeds up the process of fermentation *[1 mark]*.
Q3 60-70 atmospheres *[1 mark]*

Page 77 — Carboxylic Acids
Q1 ethanoic acid *[1 mark]*
Q2a) carbon dioxide *[1 mark]*
b) sodium carbonate + methanoic acid → sodium methanoate + water + carbon dioxide *[1 mark]*

Page 78 — Esters
Q1

[1 mark]

Page 79 — Addition Polymers
Q1

[1 mark]

Page 80 — Polyesters
Q1 dicarboxylic acids *[1 mark]* and diols *[1 mark]*
Q2 water/H_2O *[1 mark]*

Index

Index

The Periodic Table

Key

Relative atomic mass →	1
	H
	Hydrogen
Atomic number →	1

Periods	Group 1	Group 2												Group 3	Group 4	Group 5	Group 6	Group 7	Group 0
	+1	+2												+3		−3	−2	−1	
1																			4 **He** Helium 2
2	7 **Li** Lithium 3	9 **Be** Beryllium 4												11 **B** Boron 5	12 **C** Carbon 6	14 **N** Nitrogen 7	16 **O** Oxygen 8	19 **F** Fluorine 9	20 **Ne** Neon 10
3	23 **Na** Sodium 11	24 **Mg** Magnesium 12												27 **Al** Aluminium 13	28 **Si** Silicon 14	31 **P** Phosphorus 15	32 **S** Sulfur 16	35.5 **Cl** Chlorine 17	40 **Ar** Argon 18
4	39 **K** Potassium 19	40 **Ca** Calcium 20	45 **Sc** Scandium 21	48 **Ti** Titanium 22	51 **V** Vanadium 23	52 **Cr** Chromium 24	55 **Mn** Manganese 25	56 **Fe** Iron 26	59 **Co** Cobalt 27	59 **Ni** Nickel 28	63.5 **Cu** Copper 29	65 **Zn** Zinc 30		70 **Ga** Gallium 31	73 **Ge** Germanium 32	75 **As** Arsenic 33	79 **Se** Selenium 34	80 **Br** Bromine 35	84 **Kr** Krypton 36
5	85 **Rb** Rubidium 37	88 **Sr** Strontium 38	89 **Y** Yttrium 39	91 **Zr** Zirconium 40	93 **Nb** Niobium 41	96 **Mo** Molybdenum 42	98 **Tc** Technetium 43	101 **Ru** Ruthenium 44	103 **Rh** Rhodium 45	106 **Pd** Palladium 46	108 **Ag** Silver 47	112 **Cd** Cadmium 48		115 **In** Indium 49	119 **Sn** Tin 50	122 **Sb** Antimony 51	128 **Te** Tellurium 52	127 **I** Iodine 53	131 **Xe** Xenon 54
6	133 **Cs** Caesium 55	137 **Ba** Barium 56	139 **La** Lanthanum 57	178 **Hf** Hafnium 72	181 **Ta** Tantalum 73	184 **W** Tungsten 74	186 **Re** Rhenium 75	190 **Os** Osmium 76	192 **Ir** Iridium 77	195 **Pt** Platinum 78	197 **Au** Gold 79	201 **Hg** Mercury 80		204 **Tl** Thallium 81	207 **Pb** Lead 82	209 **Bi** Bismuth 83	209 **Po** Polonium 84	210 **At** Astatine 85	222 **Rn** Radon 86
7	223 **Fr** Francium 87	226 **Ra** Radium 88	227 **Ac** Actinium 89	261 **Rf** Rutherfordium 104	262 **Db** Dubnium 105	266 **Sg** Seaborgium 106	264 **Bh** Bohrium 107	277 **Hs** Hassium 108	268 **Mt** Meitnerium 109	271 **Ds** Darmstadtium 110	272 **Rg** Roentgenium 111								